TOBACCO DICTIONARY

MID-CENTURY
REFERENCE LIBRARY

DAGOBERT D. RUNES, Ph.D., *General Editor*

AVAILABLE

Dictionary of Ancient History
Dictionary of the Arts
Dictionary of European History
Dictionary of Foreign Words
and Phrases
Dictionary of Linguistics
Dictionary of Mysticism
Dictionary of Mythology
Dictionary of Philosophy
Dictionary of Psychoanalysis
Dictionary of Science and Technology
Dictionary of Sociology
Dictionary of Word Origins
Dictionary of World Literature
Encyclopedia of Aberrations
Encyclopedia of the Arts
Encyclopedia of Atomic Energy

Encyclopedia of Criminology
Encyclopedia of Literature
Encyclopedia of Psychology
Encyclopedia of Religion
Encyclopedia of Substitutes and
Synthetics
Encyclopedia of Vocational Guidance
Illustrated Technical Dictionary
Labor Dictionary
Liberal Arts Dictionary
Military and Naval Dictionary
New Dictionary of American History
New Dictionary of Psychology
Protestant Dictionary
Slavonic Encyclopedia
Theatre Dictionary
Tobacco Dictionary

FORTHCOMING

Beethoven Encyclopedia
Dictionary of American Folklore
Dictionary of American Grammar
and Usage
Dictionary of American Literature
Dictionary of American Maxims
Dictionary of American Proverbs
Dictionary of American Superstitions
Dictionary of American Synonyms
Dictionary of Anthropology
Dictionary of Arts and Crafts
Dictionary of Asiatic History
Dictionary of Astronomy
Dictionary of Child Guidance
Dictionary of Christian Antiquity
Dictionary of Discoveries and Inventions
Dictionary of Etiquette
Dictionary of Forgotten Words
Dictionary of French Literature
Dictionary of Geography
Dictionary of Geriatrics

Dictionary of German Literature
Dictionary of Hebrew Literature
Dictionary of Judaism
Dictionary of Last Words
Dictionary of Latin Literature
Dictionary of Mathematics
Dictionary of Mechanics
Dictionary of Mental Hygiene
Dictionary of New Words
Dictionary of Physical Education
Dictionary of Russian Literature
Dictionary of Science
Dictionary of Social Science
Dictionary of Spanish Literature
Dictionary of the American Language
Encyclopedia of American Philosophy
Encyclopedia of Morals
Encyclopedia of Pastoral Psychology
Personnel Dictionary
Teachers' Dictionary
Writers' Dictionary

P. 497

1 Petum [Tobacco] house
2 Negro who tears the tobacco-part
3 Negro who twists it.

4 Negro who rolls it.
5 Negro who scrapes the manioc [caffava]
6 Mill to grind the manioc.
7 Ancient method of grinding the manioc

FACTORY-YARD

8 The Press.
9 Negress sifting the flour.
10 Negress who cooks the caffava
11 The house of the master

12 The kitchen
13 Caffava drying
14 Coroso-tree.

The Earliest Known Illustration Showing An American Tobacco-Factory, From the HISTOIRE GENERALE DES ANTILLES, by Father Jean Baptiste Du Tertre, Paris, 1667-1671.

—Arents Tobacco Collection, New York Public Library.

TOBACCO
DICTIONARY

Edited by Raymond Jahn

PHILOSOPHICAL LIBRARY
New York

Printed in the United States of America

FOREWORD

When the compiler of the *Tobacco Dictionary*, Mr. Raymond Jahn, told me that he was projecting this work, I was glad to have him use the materials in the Arents Tobacco Collection of the New York Public Library in his research. So far as I knew, no attempt had been made to draw up and print in one volume, in English, a list of the terms and names which relate to the vast field of tobacco. There are, of course, many books written on the subject, and some of these have indexes. But that is not at all the same thing as a dictionary with definitions. I feel that this book will provide an answer to many questions, and give information which has previously been scattered and difficult for the average person to find, since the reference works containing it are extensive and not easily accessible. The *Tobacco Dictionary* should be useful to the student, to people in the tobacco industry and to the reading public in general.

Sarah Dickson
Curator, Arents Tobacco Collection
New York Public Library

INTRODUCTION

Few subjects have been of such widespread interest to countless numbers of people and yet received so little attention. Tobacco has an exciting history. It has helped build empires, has been intimately associated with politics, religion and finance, and has a special interest to Americans. Distinctly a product of the New World, tobacco not only played an important role in the development of this country but has, almost since the establishment of the Virginia Colony, been one of our biggest crops. While some may deplore the fact that tobacco ever appeared, many will attest to the pleasure which it has brought. Certainly it has become an integral part of our social and economic and sometimes of our moral life. It is time we knew more about it.

This book seeks to bring to the smoker the interesting, curious and necessary facts relating to the history, manufacture and use of tobacco. It includes information about all forms of tobacco—facts compiled from the most authoritative sources available. In this dictionary we have tried to cover the subject adequately, but it is not intended as a variorum. Nevertheless we hope it will bring to the tobacco raiser, the merchant and fellow smokers both pleasure and information not readily available in any other form.

ACKNOWLEDGMENT

It would be difficult to mention by name all those individuals who have offered suggestions or provided material for this book, but I am most deeply indebted to Miss Sarah Dickson, Curator of the Arents Tobacco Collection of the New York Public Library, who placed the resources of that wonderful collection at my disposal and who so graciously offered encouragement and help. And I wish specifically to thank these following people for the interest and trouble they have taken in contributing first-hand information to this work: Mr. D. R. Browning, of the Agricultural Experiment Station, West Virginia University; Mr. P. M. Cox, Assistant County Agricultural Agent, North Carolina State College; Mr. F. A. Greenhut, of the General Cigar Company; Mr. S. N. Hawks, Jr., Agronomy Extension Specialist at the State College Station, Raleigh, North Carolina; Mr. W. S. Koenig, Director of Public Relations, the R. J. Reynolds Tobacco Company; Mr. Ralph Lasbury, Director of the Shade Tobacco Growers' Association; Mr. W. B. Ogden, Professor of Horticulture, the University of Wisconsin; the Production Department of Philip Morris & Co.; Mr. Eugene L. Raymond, Executive Director of the Cigar Institute of America; Mr. W. D. Valleau, of the Agricultural Experiment Station, University of Kentucky; and Mr. Morris Wurman, Vice President of the Bayuk Cigar Company.

I would like to take this opportunity also to thank the many individuals of the several state agricultural services and the United States Department of Agriculture who have helped secure information for me or who have contributed to the writing of the many periodicals consulted.

And I wish to thank the following authors whose works I have referred to, and their publishers who have been kind enough to permit the use of the information taken from these books: The American Dialect Society and Dr. L. R. Dinqus for his "Tobacco Words"; the Art Printing Company for Willis N. Baer's THE ECONOMIC DEVELOPMENT OF THE CIGAR INDUSTRY IN THE UNITED STATES; the Cigar Institute of America for THE STORY OF CIGARS; J. J. Berliner & Staff for several manuals and extracts on tobacco and tobacco products; Columbia University Press for its publication AMERICAN SPEECH; Miss May Coult, whose DICTIONARY OF THE CUBAN TOBACCO INDUSTRY is published by the Government and Dr. Perdomo for his contribution to this work; Harcourt Brace & Co. for Count Corti's A HISTORY OF SMOKING; Alfred A. Knopf, Inc. and Joseph C. Robert for his fine THE STORY OF TOBACCO IN AMERICA; the Macmillan Company, for Alfred Dunhill's THE PIPE BOOK and Eric Patridge's A DICTIONARY OF SLANG AND UNCONVENTIONAL ENGLISH; the State of North Carolina for the publication, "Tobacco in North Carolina: Growing, Marketing and Processing," and the North Carolina Department of Agriculture for THE TOBACCO STORY; and the University of North Carolina Press for Nannie May Tilley's THE BRIGHT TOBACCO INDUSTRY; W. & J. Rounce, Ltd., for C. L. Constantinides' A MANUAL FOR PLANTERS, DEALERS AND MANUFACTURERS; Sir Isaac Pitman, Ltd., for Arthur Edmund Tanner's TOBACCO FROM THE GROWER TO THE SMOKER; the Tobacco Leaf Publishing Company for Mr. Carl Avery Warner's TOBACCOLAND; and The Tobacco Merchants of the U. S. for their "Tobacco Manual"; Twayne Publishers, Inc., for the terms taken from the DICTIONARY OF AMERICAN UNDERWORLD LINGO; the Virginia Polytechnic Institute for a number of its publications on tobacco; Federal-State Crop Reporting Service for its bulletin, "Wisconsin Tobacco Production and Marketing"; and the Yale University Press for Tennant's THE AMERICAN CIGARETTE INDUSTRY.

R. JAHN

MAYAN PRIEST
SMOKING TUBE-PIPE

This representation of a Mayan priest
smoking a crude tubular sort of pipe was
taken from a carving. Mayan priests may
be presumed to have used tobacco in con-
junction with certain religious ceremonies.

—*Alfred Dunhill's "The Pipe Book,"* (Macmillan)

Tobacco Growth and Use

CLASS AND TYPE	PRODUCTION AREAS	CHIEF USE
Class 1, Flue-Cured Types		
Type 11: Old Belt flue-cured	Piedmont section of Virginia and North Carolina.	Cigarettes, pipe and chewing tobacco and for export.
Type 12: Eastern North Carolina flue-cured	Coastal sections of North Carolina, north of the South River.	
Type 13: South Carolina flue-cured	Coastal setions of South Carolina and the southeastern counties of North Carolina, south of the South River.	
Type 14: Georgia and Florida flue-cured	Southern Georgia and northern Florida.	
Class 2, Fire-Cured Types		
Type 21: Virginia fire-cured	Piedmont and mountain sections of Virginia.	For export, manufacture of snuff, and plug wrappers.
Type 22: Tennessee-Kentucky fire-cured	Produced in a section east of the Tennessee River, in southern Kentucky and northern Tennessee.	
Type 23: Kentucky-Tennessee fire-cured	Produced in a section between the Tennessee, Ohio, and Mississippi Rivers in western Kentucky and northwestern Tennessee.	
Type 24: Henderson Stemming of Northern fire-cured	Webster, Hopkins, McLean, Union, and Henderson Counties of Kentucky.	
Class 3, Air-Cured Types		As below:
Light air-cured		
Type 31: Burley	Kentucky, Tennessee, Ohio, Indiana, West Virginia, Virginia, North Carolina, and Missouri.	Cigarettes, pipe and chewing tobacco.
Type 32: Southern Maryland	Five counties of southern Maryland—Prince Georges, Anne Arundel, Calvert, Charles, and St. Marys.	Cigarettes and export.
Dark air-cured		
Type 35: One Sucker	North-central Tennessee and south-central Kentucky.	Chewing, plug and export.
Type 36: Green River	Northern part of Kentucky in the territory adjacent to Owensboro and Henderson.	
Type 37: Virginia sun-cured	Central Virginia, north of the James River.	
Class 4, Cigar-Filler Types		
Type 41: Pennsylvania Seedleaf	Lancaster County, Pa., and the adjoining counties.	Cigar filler.
Type 42: Gebhardt	Miami Valley section of Ohio and extending into Indiana.	
Type 43: Zimmer	Miami Valley section of Ohio and extending into Indiana.	
Type 44: Dutch	Miami Valley section of Ohio.	
Type 46: Puerto Rican sun-grown, including primed (Deshojado) and stalk-cut (Mata)	Island of Puerto Rico.	

Class 5, Cigar-Binder Types		
Type 51 : Connecticut Broadleaf	Connecticut Valley sections of Connecticut and Massachusetts.	Cigar binder.
Type 52 : Connecticut Havana Seed	Connecticut and Housatonic Valley sections of Connecticut and Massachusetts.	
Type 53 : New York and Pennsylvania Havana Seed	Big Flats and Onondago sections of New York, extending into Pennsylvania.	
Class 5, Binder Types, Cont.		
Type 54 : Southern Wisconsin	Wisconsin, south and east of Wisconsin river.	Cigar Binder
Type 55 : Northern Wisconsin	Wisconsin, north and west of the Wisconsin River, and in eastern Minnesota.	
Type 56 : Georgia and Florida sun-grown	Southwestern Georgia and north-central Florida.	
Class 6, Cigar Wrapper Types		
Type 61 : Connecticut Shade	Connecticut Valley sections of Connecticut and Massachusetts.	Cigar wrapper.
Type 62 : Georgia and Florida Shade-Grown	Southwestern Georgia and north-central Florida.	
Miscellaneous Types		
Type 72 : Louisiana Perique	Southeastern Louisiana.	Smoking.
Type 73 : All domestic types of tobacco not otherwise classified.		

A table of United States Tobacco, its Classes and Types, where grown, and its chief uses. Government standardization of American tobacco types and classes has helped both grower and buyer. The Type refers to broad units which are further broken down into Classes. These are determined by the curing method employed, the area in which the leaf is raised, and the variety of seed used. Classes are further divided into grades, which are determined by quality, size, condition, color, etc.

—*The Crop Reporting Service of the Wisconsin and United States Departments of Agriculture.*

TOBACCO DICTIONARY

A

A-shaped bed

A long narrow permanent seed bed used in Canada. The A-shaped bed is permanently covered with a sloping glass roof forming a sort of greenhouse.

Abridora (opener)

In the Cuban industry, the person who strips leaves from the stalks of the tobacco plant.

Absorbants

1) Filters used to intercept some of the tobacco ingredients from the smoke, especially the oleo-resins.

2) A preparation sprinkled or dusted over loose processed tobacco to improve its ability to hold moisture. Silica or alumina hydrogel, kisselguhr, fuller's earth, etc., may be used for this purpose.

Actual weight

The weight of tobacco at any time after it is packed. Thus the term refers only to ordered and usually to air-cured tobacco.

Adams, John Quincy (1767-1848)

The sixth President of the United States. He was in sympathy with the Anti-Tobacco movement of 1830-1860 and made it known that he had successfully broken the smoking habit. It seems that in his twenties he was quite fond of West Indian cigars and was even considered a connoisseur of them.

Adcock, P. Arthur

A hybrid variety of flue-cured tobaccos of large and rather fibrous leaves.

Adrianople

A Turkish tobacco of neutral flavour, grown on the Thracian plains in Turkey, usually of average quality of the ova baschi-bagli type. Used as a blend for pipe tobaccos.

1

Adulterants

see IMPROVEMENTS

Africans

Tobacco grown mostly in Kentucky, prepared principally for West African trade.

Aging

After the tobacco is cured, it is packed in casks known as hogsheads, which are stored in warehouses. They remain there for at least a year. This is done in order to give the tobacco its mellowness. Aging also means what is technically known as fermentation or sweating of leaf tobacco.

Air-cured

Tobacco is cured by hanging it in curing barns where the circulation of air is especially good and little or no artificial heat is introduced.

The tobacco is placed in the barn, usually after wilting, and it is cured without the use of artificial heat simply by regulating the ventilation. One of the most important factors is to regulate properly the rate of drying. If dried too rapidly the leaf is killed and the curing process stopped. If the leaf is killed by bruising, rapid drying, or too high heating, there is no means of removing the natural starch in the leaf, and the tobacco is harsh, lifeless and "strawy."

Nearly all the cigar tobaccos, and the greater portion of Burley and other manufacturing tobaccos grown in Kentucky and the adjoining states, as well as the Virginia and Maryland sun-cured types are air-cured.

Charcoal or gas fires may, if necessary, be used to supplement the natural curing process.

Air-cured Tobacco

This type of tobacco is divided into two groups, a light one and a dark one. The light group includes the Burley, which is grown in Kentucky, Tennessee, Virginia, North Carolina, Missouri, West Virginia, Indiana, and Ohio. Maryland is also a member of the light group. Both Burley and Maryland are used for the manufacture of cigarettes. The darker group, which is used mainly for the production of chewing tobacco, includes Green River, Virginia's Sun-Cured and One-Sucker.

Air-cured tobacco is graded class three, by the Dept. of Agriculture of the United States Government.

Under the government classification, air-cured tobaccos include types 31, Burley; 31-V, Low-Nicotine Burley; 32, Southern Maryland leaf; 35, One-Sucker; 36, Green River; and 37, Virginia Sun-Cured.

Air-dried

Unfermented tobacco, customarily prepared for storage under natural atmospheric conditions.

Alabama Bright

Common name for one of the flue-cured tobaccos produced principally in the southern section of Georgia and to some extent in Florida, Alabama and Mississippi. Government classified as Type 14 of Class 1.

Alderman

Eighteenth century English term for a Yard of Clay pipe. *See* YARD OF CLAY.

Algodon

A type of cigarette paper made from a cotton base.

Algonquin pipe

A tube pipe of the early Algonquin burial mounds excavated in Ohio and Virginia. The pipe consisted of a tube of bone, stone, wood or cane.

Allyl alcohol

A liquid weed killer used in flue-cured tobacco areas.

Amarillo

(Yellow) The Cuban term for a grade of filler group tobacco from the Vuelta Abajo District, used principally for cigarettes.

Ambassadours Hearbe

see HERBE DU GRAND PRIEUR

American Tobacco Company

Incorporated in 1890, in New Jersey, with James Buchanan Duke as its first president, this company controlled nine-tenths of the United States cigarette manufacture. Within a period of twenty years the company controlled four-fifths of the entire tobacco industry with the exception of cigars. However in 1911, the Supreme Court declared that the company was a monopoly in restraint of trade. The company was therefore ordered to dissolve. It was then re-organized as fourteen separate companies, with one of them retaining the name of the original company.

Anatolian

Turkish tobacco raised in the north-west section of that country, frequently sold under the name Gonen, Ismid, Hendek, Dusdje or Broussa. Used in blending pipe tobaccos.

Andullo (plug tobacco)

A dense heavy leaf of tobacco raised in the Dominican Republic, used for cigarette and pipe smoking.

In Cuba, plug tobacco or pressed tobacco prepared for chewing.

Angouleme

see HERBE ANGOULMOISINE

Angular leaf spot

See BLACKFIRE

Antarctick Bugloss

see BUGLOSSUM ANTARCTICUM

A 17th Century name for a variety of tobacco, based on the resemblance of leaves of the plant to those of the ox-tongue (French, buglosse).

Anthracnose

Caused by *Colletotrichum* sp., a fungus disease attacking mature plants, generally found in Maryland. The disease produces numerous light-colored spots on the leaves, and the lower surface of the midrib and lateral veins have red-brown, elongated lesions. When severely affected, the leaves are puckered and the plant is stunted. Particularly likely to appear on plants which have been flooded.

Anti-Tobacconists

Anti-tobacco sentiments have been voiced in every country as soon as the use of tobacco became general. In the United States such sentiments were first expressed by the Puritans, who found tobacco loathsome to the eye, and hateful to the lungs.

The most famous of all anti-tobacco tracts is undoubtedly James I's *Counterblaste* against the use of tobacco in his dominions, but many famous people have strongly opposed tobacco in any form—including Henry Ward Beecher, Horace Greeley, J. Q. Adams, George Bernard Shaw, etc.

The anti-tobacco movements in America have been closely associated with the prohibition movement, first appearing after the turn of the nineteenth cenury. Anti-tobacco sentiments, however, were largely dissipated by the Civil War and the First World War, despite the alleged horrors and dangers to which tobacco users were said to be subject. At one time the use of alcohol was itself imputed to tobacco, for it was alleged that the frequenting of places where tobacco was smoked led to the practice of sipping at the soda fountain, the taking of beer and eventually (and inevitably) of even stronger drinks. Descriptions depicting the foul discharge of the tobacco user and the diseases (including cancer and epilepsy) were gruesome enough in detail.

Such strong anti-tobacconists as Lucy Page Garton, who during the Prohibition movement, succeeded in arousing Chicago youth to scorn and sometimes active persecution of smokers, did a great deal to abate the use of tobacco in this country at that time. Churches and public spirited citizens were generally aroused in righteous indignation, and it became difficult for any prominent person to refrain from taking a stand on the tobacco issue. In 1920 Kansas forbade the smoking of cigarettes, and several other states prepared to follow suit.

Meeting the onslaught with financial backing and skillful advertising, tobacco interests joined hands with liberals and tobacco habitués. Effective as their methods may have been, however, the anti-tobacco movement may be said to have died of natural causes. The number of persons who smoked steadily increased, with the popularization of cigarettes and Womens' Suffrage, and by the First World War the press reflected but little opposition to the use of tobacco. Public sentiment seems finally to have accepted what James I had referred to as "the Stigian smoke."

Apooke

A Native Virginian term for tobacco.

In *The Historie of Travaile into Virginia Britannica,* published by the Hakluyt Society between 1610 and 1612, Strachey says, "Here is great store of tobacco, which the salvages call *apooke* . . . (the salvages take) the same in pipes of earth, which very ingeniously they can make."

Apron

Screen wire-type conveyor which carries cigarette tobacco through strip, ordering and drying machine.

Apron machine

A redrying machine through which a conveyor belt carries loose tobacco, originally developed by Josiah K. Proctor in 1895.

See STICK MACHINE

Arique

The strip from the base of Cuban royal palm leaves used to tie bundles of tobacco.

Army Rations

In 1864 a law was finally passed in the Confederate States providing one ration of tobacco for each Confederate soldier. (The Navy had for some years received rations of tobacco.) Tobacco and Northern coffee were the standard "swap" through the picket lines of the Civil War.

Aroma

The fragrance of a cigar—the "bouquet." Aroma should not be confused with the strength of a cigar, which may be very mild and rich in aroma or strong and lacking in it.

As is

Tobacco sold without any guarantee as to condition, whether it is free from damage, rot or must.

Atados

A bundle of fifty-one Spanish cigars, generally made at the King's factory at Seville, Spain.

Auction

The sale of tobacco to the highest bidder or the place where such a sale is conducted. The first auction (of hogshead tobacco) was conducted at Lynchburg, Virginia, before 1810, and within twenty-five years this system became dominant, though very little flue-cured tobacco is now sold in hogsheads.

Austria

Tobacco appeared in Austria after the Thirty Years War and its use spread through even the ruling houses by 1650. Legal measures were almost immediately taken to stamp out the practice of smoking. In 1652 a decree of the Diet of Moravia forbade its use, followed by other edicts of a similar nature. Despite these, however, the habit made its way into the very heart of the opposition. In 1656 it was discovered that certain of the priests had taken up smoking. Reactionary measures appear to have stimulated the use of tobacco, however, for the custom spread from Bohemia to Vienna and so continued beyond Austria's eastern borders.

Aya-Solouk

The area in the Smyrna district (ancient Ephesus), near the Aegean Sea, which produces the most aromatic types of Turkish tobacco.

B

Baai
Coarse cut smoking tobacco made almost entirely of Java leaf, used in large-bowl clay pipes in The Netherlands.

Bacterial wilt
A bacterial disease attacking many plants besides tobacco. The germ enters the plant through the roots and multiplies so rapidly that the water-conducting vessels become clogged, causing the leaves to wither and perish. The woody part of the stalk shows a yellowish to black streak when the bark is stripped off. Also called Tobacco Wilt and Granville Wilt, *which see.*

Baffra
A Turkish tobacco similar to Samsoun and grown in the same region, close to the town of Baffra. The leaf, however, is almost stemless and the flavour is stronger. *Baffra* is used as a blending agent for pipe tobaccos.

Bahia
A leaf raised in the Bahia Province in Brazil. *Bahia* produces about half of all Brazilian tobaccos, which are said to have been brought there from Cuba in the early Colonial days. *Bahia* leaf is small, sweet, dark and mild.

Bale
A fifty to sixty pound case of unfermented Turkish tobacco is called a bale, as opposed to a smaller case called a ballot. Bales are wrapped in woollen matting before shipping.

Pennsylvania tobacco is also baled and usually weighs about seventy-five pounds.

Bale of Hay
A package of cigarettes (slang).

Bale Press
A large box with collapsible sides, lined with paper, and

equipped with a pressing mechanism, used in the domestic cigar tobacco industry. Pressed bales contain about seventy pounds of tobacco pressed into bales before being sent to market.

Ball

Balls which were formed of tobacco, coarsely spun into a kind of thick twist. They were about the size of a man's head and similar to the so-called "Varinas"—the "best" tobacco exported by the Spaniards, from Varinas in Venezuela.

Balloon frame barn

A type of tobacco barn which can be constructed without mortising. It will hold about three acres of leaf, is thirty-four by sixty-four feet.

Ballot

A small wooden case containing unfermented Turkish tobacco, usually weighing twenty-five to thirty pounds. Such cases are covered with white cloth before shipping. The ballot should not contain any inferior grade leaf.

Banda

(Stemmed binder). The stemmed binder used in better Cuban cigars.

Bar

A form of tobacco made into a cake by pressing loose leaf in a metal frame. The hard block of leaf-mass is covered with a wrapper leaf and again is pressed into the shape of a rectangular bar, with the trademark embossed on the wrapper. It is usually made from dark Cavendish tobaccos and used for chewing or smoking tobacco.

Favored in Britain.

Barn

The barn or building in which tobacco is cured. The dimension is more or less standard at sixteen, twenty-one or twenty-five feet square in order to permit the hanging of four or five or six rows of tobacco.

The smallest barn will accommodate about 50,000 leaves, or the priming from thirty acres.

Barn filler
The person employed to hang green tobacco strung on laths in the curing barns.

Barn-rot
The decay in tobacco while it is still in the barn. Spoilage in this stage is caused by too much moisture and too little ventilation.

Barn tender
The person appointed to take care of the barn during the curing process.

Baschi-bagli
(Literally, tied at the head). The second grade of Turkish leaves, only slightly larger than the *basma*; taken from near the top of the plant. Leaves of this grade are mostly used for blending smoking tobaccos. Better grades of *Baschi-bagli* are also termed *basma*.

Basibali
One of the two main types of Turkish tobacco, the other being Basma. The Basibali plant is larger than the Basma and has coarser leaves which are attached to the stalk with a short stem. Sold in Britain as Persichan.

Basket
The shallow woven wooden container which holds different grades of tobacco for the market. Also, as a verb, to put tobacco into such a basket or to basket it. A basket may hold from a few to several hundred pounds of marketable tobacco.

Basma
(Literally, pressed). One of the two main types of Turkish tobaccos, the other being *Basibali*. The Basma plant is small— two to three feet. Its leaves, two to ten inches long, do not have stems but grow on the stalk of the plant. There are generally eight rows of three leaves on each mature stalk. On the English market, bales of leaves from the bottom rows of the Basma plant are sold as *Basma*. Top leaves are sold as Dubec. *Basma* does not include *Dip*, which see, 2nd definition.

Bed

The area especially prepared for sowing tobacco seed. Also called plant bed, tobacco bed, or seed bed.

The tobacco bed is best described as a cold frame.

Bedded

A term of the bright tobacco industry to describe fields which have been laid off in well fertilized rows preparatory to receiving the transplanted tobacco.

See HILLS

Bell's Number One

A hybrid selection of flue-cured tobaccos from Bottom Special crossed with Four Hundred Two. A large-stalk of medium height and large, broad leaves of an upright growth characterize this selection. Cured leaves are rich lemon to orange in color.

Bell's Number Two

A hybrid selection of flue-cured tobaccos from Bottom Special and Oxford 26. Similar to Bell's Number One, with the leaves slightly puckered along the veins and midrib and of a yellowish cast.

Beltsville soils

A sandy loam soil with a fairly compact sub-soil and sandy loam surface six to twelve inches deep.

Bent

A style of pipe characterized by a considerable curve in the stem. The bowl of the Bent is round and the shank rises from its base at about a forty-five degree angle. The stem is half-curved.

Berro

Literally, watercress, the Cuban term for a light green cigarette paper.

Best leaves

In flue-cured tobaccos, choice leaves taken from the center of the plant.

Betun

A liquid of secret formula sprayed on Havana tobaccos to aid in the fermentation of the leaf.

Bidi

A form of cigar smoked extensively in India, consisting of granulated tobacco rolled in a section of the leaf of a species of Indian ebony and tied with a thread.

Big Cuban

A selection of domestic Cuban wrapper leaf shade-grown in the Florida-Georgia wrapper region.

Big root

The name by which root knot nematode is known in the flue-cured regions.

See ROOT KNOT NEMATODE

Big Three

In 1941 the government charged the Big Three, as the American Tobacco Company, Liggett & Myers and R. J. Reynolds were called, with combination and conspiracy to fix prices and with monopolizing the cigarette industry.

Bihar

A form of Bright tobacco which proved to be adaptable to the Bihar region in India. Little of this tobacco is exported.

Binder

A single leaf of tobacco wound around the filler of the cigar to hold it together. Most binder leaves are raised in the United States, chiefly in Wisconsin, Pennsylvania, New York and the Connecticut Valley.

Bird's-eye

A variety of bar tobacco popular in Britain which includes small portions of fine leaf stalk. The surface of the bar bears a resemblance to birds' eyes. This is generally dark, hard and sweet, and is used for smoking and chewing tobaccos.

Birdwood

A cigarette (slang).

Bit

The mouth end of a pipe stem, sometimes a separate part. In England, the Mouthpiece.

Black cigars

English classification for cigars made from Brazilian tobacco.

See WHITE CIGARS.

Black Fat

A processed tobacco greatly in demand around the turn of the century for export. Black Fat is made of One-Sucker or fire-cured varieties. The leaf is so treated as to produce a tough black oily product sold almost exclusively on the west coast of Africa.

Blackfire

A plant-bed disease caused by *Pseudomonas angulata* (Fromme & Murray) Holland, which causes small lesions or light colored dead areas. The disease can cause serious crop damage and is more easily prevented than eliminated.

Black leg

See BLACK SHANK.

Black patch

The western tobacco district of Kentucky and Tennessee. This area was the center of the tobacco war of the first decade of this century.

Black root rot

A rot characterized by a blackening in the roots, common in most tobacco-growing states, especially where lime is used in preparing the soil.

Black shank

One of the most destructive of the tobacco diseases. It is caused by a soil fungus which may attack the plant at any stage of growth. Discoloration of the affected stalk and roots is followed by the death and wilting of the plant.

Black tobacco

Generally a synonym for dark tobacco, though the term is sometimes applied to export tobaccos.

Blackwell, Wm. T. (1839-1903)

Developed the business of John Ruffin Green and applied modern production and distribution techniques. Due to him, the famous Durham Bull became known throughout the world, and his establishment grew to be the largest smoking-tobacco factory in the world, in 1884.

Blanket

Prison slang for the cigarette paper used in "twisting one" or "making a pill."

Blankets

Cigarette papers (slang).

Blankets and Freckles

Materials for a cigarette (slang).

Blend

The combination of different classes and types of tobacco to produce a desired flavor, aroma or burn. The blend of most cigarettes and smoking tobaccos is kept secret.

Blending

Process of proportioning various types and grades to obtain its desired flavor and "burn."

Blight

See LEAF SPOT DISEASES.

Blistering

A greenish-black color produced in flue-cured tobaccos from too quick an increase in the temperature during the curing process.

Bloomrape

A parasite occurring chiefly in the blue-grass region of Kentucky on farms on which hemp has been grown. It attaches itself to the roots of hemp, tobacco, and other plants and may do serious injury.

Blue Mold

A fungus disease which causes great destruction in the seedbeds, where it has been prevalent in nearly all tobacco-growing areas. It first appears as a circular patch of yellow on the leaves and may show on the underside a fungus growth of a pale white or violet color.

Blue Pryor

A strain of dark-fired tobacco which produces a heavy yield of long, broad, small-fibered leaves.

Blunt

A trade term for a rather slender cigar smaller than a corona but not as small as a thin or a cigarillo. Like a corona the blunt has a straight-cut tuck end.

Bobbins

A round roll of cigarette paper the width of the manufactured cigarette. Paper from the bobbin is fed into the cigarette machine. There is sufficient paper on a bobbin to manufacture over eight thousand cigarettes.

Body

The thickness and density of leaf or weight per unit of surface.

Boer

A style of pipe distinguished by the thickness of its shank which seems to be an extension of almost the entire side of the bowl. The shank joins the bowl near the top and tapers gently to the bottom, curving out to meet the stem, which is generally straight.

Boiler

A smoking pipe (slang).

Boite nature

The Cuban term for a plain (unwrapped) wooden cigar box made of Honduran cedar.

Bonanza

A flue-cured tobacco of the Orinoco variety suitable to medium or light soils. On more fertile soils the leaf will cure dark to orange, lemon color on more sandy soils. The plant is of medium height, the leaves broad at the base and tapering to a sharp point.

Bonche

(Bunch). The mold used to bunch cigar fillers in small Cuban shops and factories.

Bonchero

The lowest class of Cuban cigar maker who has to use a mold in order to fashion his filler properly. *Boncheros* generally make *brevas* and similar small-sized cigars.

Bonded Factory

A distinction as to type of tobacco factory in England. In the bonded factory tobacco is received duty-free and duty is paid instead on the manufactured goods. Bonded factories are generally limited to domestic consumption, producing mostly Cavendish-smoking tobacco. Such factories are under the careful supervision of customs' authorities.

See EXCISE FACTORY

Bonsack Cigarette Machine

The first practical machine for the shaping, rolling and cutting of cigarettes. Invented by James Albert Bonsack, of Virginia, and first patented in 1881 (registered in 1880). It was the best of the early cigarette manufacturing machines. It was used by many prominent tobacco manufacturers such as Allen & Ginter of Richmond, the Blackwell firm of Durham, and W. Duke, Sons & Company. However the Dukes were the first to really use it on a large scale. Their model, which was set up in 1884, at Durham, produced 120,000 cigarettes per day, using only three people. This was about fifty times the rate of the hand operators. In 1884, fourteen such machines—Bonsack machines—were in use in America and Europe.

Booking

In the cigar industry, making a pad of binder or wrapper leaves.

Bookman

see TICKET-MAKER.

Boots

Slang expression peculiar to Virginia indicating trash.

Bordeaux

The common name for a preventative against various plant-bed diseases, notably Wildfire and Blackfire. It is prepared with copper sulfate, hydrated lime and water.

Botched

The grade of any tobacco which, through improper preparation, cannot conform to the usual market standards for that type. Disorderly or irregularly tied or extreme mixtures would come under this heading.

Bote

(Canister). Broken or nondescript tobacco and scrap of the leaf grown in the Remedios region in Cuba.

Bottom Special

Same as Three Sucker.

Bouw

A small tobacco field in Java of one and three-quarters acres. The Bouw is tended by a trained Chinese coolie and Javanese assistants. Tobacco estates in Java run five to seven hundred acres.

Bowl

The receptacle for tobacco in a pipe. Frequently separate from the stem.

Boxers

Personnel who insert packs of cigarettes into cartons.

Brain Tablet

A cigarette (slang).

Brand

The name given to a specific marketable product, which has been blended according to an exact and usually secret formula. One company may produce several brands of the same type of commodity.

Brazil

Brazil ranks as the world's third largest producer of tobacco leaf, the greater portion of which is suited for cigar purposes. The bulk of these cigars are consumed in Brazil. Bahia, on the eastern coast, is the largest tobacco producing Province. Rio Grande do Sul ranks second.

Brazilian

Very fine cut Perique.

Brea

Literally resin, the Cuban term for a pale yellow cigarette paper.

Break

An auction sale of loose tobacco. The term no doubt originated in the habit of breaking open the caked mass of leaves in a hogshead of tobacco in order to sample and sell. The term is still used, however, to apply to modern loose-leaf auctions.

Break Horse

Device used to separate layers of tobacco in hogsheads for inspection.

Breaking

The practice, originating in Virginia, of sampling a hogshead of tobacco by breaking it open and extracting a selection of leaves. In more modern times, since the leaf is exhibited in a loose condition, the term "break" generally refers to the sales of tobacco at the warehouse.

Breaking (Pulling) a Pile

Pulling hands of tobacco from the middle of a pile for examination.

Breaking Suckers

Suckering or removing the suckers, the second growth of leaves after first-growth leaves have been removed.

Breaking Tops

Common term for topping: that is, for removing the blossoms of maturing plants.

Briar

The wood from which briar pipes are made: it is the root of the White Heather plant (*Erica Arborea*) found on the island of Corsica, in southern France and on the slopes of the Italian Alps.

Briar Pipe

A tobacco pipe made of Briarwood.

Bright

A term commonly indicating Virginia tobaccos; more specifically, flue-cured tobaccos, used chiefly in making cigarettes.

Bright-crop

see THIN-CROP

Bright Leaf

Center leaves of the Burley and Maryland tobacco plants.

Used for cigarettes.

see THIN-CROP

Bright Virginia Leaf

Common name for one of the flue-cured tobaccos raised principally in the Piedmont sections of Virginia and North Carolina. Classified by government standards as Type 11, Class 1.

Brissage Cigar

A long, slender cigar with a straw mouthpiece and straw through the center.

Broadleaf Tobacco

A descendant of the native tobacco raised in New England before the colonists adopted it for cultivation. At first used as a pipe tobacco, it immediately became popular as a cigar leaf, after Spanish cigars were introduced into this country about 1762—introduced, as legend would have it, by none less than the Revolutionary patriot, General Israel Putnam. Broadleaf tobacco is produced in the Connecticut Valley and government classified as Type 51. It is sold as sorted and unsorted tobacco and the entire crop is used in the manufacture of cigars. Broadleaf is commonly used as a binder in domestic Havana filler cigars.

see also CONNECTICUT BROADLEAF

Brokes

A local term for a specific grade of Broadleaf and Havana Seed cigar tobaccos, indicating leaves over 18½" long in an unsweated condition which have a potential yield of at least 50% binder cuts.

Broom

A cheap cigar (slang).

Brown Root Rot

A decay common to the northern areas, particularly Wisconsin and the Connecticut Valley. Symptoms and associations are similar to meadow nematode.

Brown Spot

A disease attacking maturing leaves, characterized by a brown spot. The lesions are rather large and tend to be circular, frequently marked by concentric rings. Brown spot commonly attacks flue-cured tobacco in western North Carolina and Virginia when the harvest period is wet.

Buba blanca

(White pustule). A nematode which attacks Cuban tobacco plants.

Budworm

(*Heliothis virescens* Fabr.). An insect pest especially destructive in the South. Control is usually effected through poisons, though parasites may be introduced. The cotton bollworm, corn ear worm and false tobacco budworm are closely related species.

Bug Dust

A cheap or inferior tobacco (slang).

Bug juice

Slang expression for insecticides used to kill harmful pests on the plants or seedlings. Derived from lugs of poor color, and irritant oils removed during heat treatments of blended tobacco.

Buglossum Antarcticum

A seventeenth century name for a variety of tobacco based on the resemblance of the leaves of the plant to those of the ox-tongue (French, buglosse).

Bulk

Orderly piles of tobacco which are ready for sorting.

In flue-cured tobaccos cured leaves are piled in bulk while still attached to the sticks. This process helps improve the color of the leaf and assists in bleaching out the green remaining after curing. Shadegrown tobaccos are piled in bulk for the first sweating or fermentation process. Each bulk of shadegrown tobacco weighs 3000 to 5000 lbs.

Bulking

The process whereby the new shade grown tobacco is conditioned before the actual work of sorting, sizing and packing the wrappers for the trade is begun in the warehouses. The newly cured tobacco is permitted to mull in the bulks for a period of at least four weeks.

Bulking agents

Organic substances used to supplant tobacco, not to be confused with adulterants, the resins, oils and sugars which are added in the manufacturing process. Bulking agents are added to dry tobacco in order to increase the weight.

Bulks

Large piles of tobacco.

Bull

Slang for Bull Durham tobacco.

Bulldog

A style of pipe with a square shank and somewhat flattened bowl beaded at the widest circumference and tapered in toward both the top and bottom. The stem continues the square appearance of the shank and terminates in a saddle-type bit. The stem is about as long as the shank and bowl together.

Bull-Gang

Slang expression common among growers and manufacturers for the laborers who handle hogsheads of tobacco, loading and unloading them, etc.

Bull Moose

A style of short pipe with an especially heavy shank and a slight curve in the shank and stem so that the bit rises to the level of the top of the round bowl.

Bunch

The cigar filler and binder before the wrapper is put on.

Bunch maker

One who shapes the bunch before it is put into the shaper or cigar mold.

Bunco (also Bunko)

A slender Asiatic cigar.

Bundle

Havana Seed or Broadleaf is prepared for the buyer in bundles containing about forty pounds of leaf. These are wrapped in heavy paper, then sent to the sorting shops and sweating rooms.

Bureau

One of the more popular snuffs presented to Louis XV

which achieved a lasting popularity, especially among cabinet ministers; hence it came to be called *Bureau.*

Burley

A type of air-cured tobacco. It is darker than flue-cured tobacco, thrives on rich soil and requires little fertilizer. Burley is now used in manufacturing cigarettes, but because of its ability to absorb large quantities of flavoring it was formerly used exclusively in smoking and chewing tobacco. Burley reaches its highest state of development in the limestone soils in the famous bluegrass region of Kentucky, in the eastern Tennessee district, and in southern Ohio. Government classified as Type 31 of Class 3. The usual grades are, 1 flyings, 2 trash, 3 lugs, 4 bright leaf, 5 red leaf, and 6 tips.

White Burley has largely replaced older varieties of the Burley plant (Standup, Twist Bud, or Red).

In modern usage, the term Burley generally refers to White Burley.

see WHITE BURLEY

Burn

The burn of a cigar is the rate of combustibility and is controlled by the organic composition of the tobacco, especially of the wrapper leaf.

Burning

Burning was the earliest method developed for sterilizing the plant-bed soil, and is still widely used.

Burro

The process of sprinkling hands of Cuban tobacco with petun to encourage the simulation of cured tobacco.

Busting the Middle

Any cultivation in flue-cured areas that works the soil between rows.

Butt

The root end of tobacco leaf.

Butt

A cigarette (American Slang).

Also, the stamp or stub of a cigar or cigarette.

Butting

Removing butt ends from bundles of leaves.

Button

Slang expression for the tip of the plant which swells before bursting into bloom.

Button Stage

The stage in the development of the Bright tobacco plant when the tops are broken off.

Byproducts

Tobacco byproducts are limited to tobacco extracts, nicotine products, nicotine-free tobacco suitable for fertilizer, and factory wastes adapted for use as nicotine dusts and fertilizers. The principal byproduct of tobacco is nicotine for horticultural and veterinarian use.

Byrd, William of Westover (1674-1744)

He was the most noted representative of the tobacco planters. Admitted to the English bar and the Royal Society, he became the agent for the colony of Virginia in England. He was also a member of the Virginia House of Burgesses. His library was notable and contained the collection of Cotton Mather. He also wrote several works. At the time of his death his properties totalled 179,000 acres.

C

Cabbage

A cheap cigar (slang).

Cabeza (head)

Cuban cigar makers' name for the tip of the cigar, i.e., the end the smoker puts in his mouth.

Cabo (stub)

The butt or stub of a cigar that has been smoked.

Cacao moth

(Ephestia Elutella). An insect which first attacked stores of cured tobacco in England in the early 1930's.

Cachimba

A type of Cuban pipe used for smoking tobacco.

Cajon

(Box or frame). In the Cuban cigar industry the term has several variations. The *Cajas de batir hebra* is the mixing box which receives shredded leaf as it emerges from the cutting machines in cigarette factories. The *Caja de tercio* is a baling frame, and *Cajas de galera* storage boxes in which blended tobaccos are kept.

Cake

see BAR

Calabash

A light-weight, graceful pipe made from the neck of a large South African gourd (*Lagenaria Vulgaris*). A mouthpiece and a bowl of meerschaum or clay are added to the gourd.

Calico

see MOSAIC

Calumet

Peace pipe or ceremonial pipe among the North American Plains Indians. The word is derived from the French form (*chalumet*) of the Latin word *calamus* or reed.

24

Camels

This American brand, which first appeared in 1913, was the first modern cigarette. A creation of the R. J. Reynolds Tobacco Company, it was a blend of flue-cured tobacco, seasoned with Turkish, and most important of all, a sweetened or cased Burley. According to chemists, it was this specially treated Burley that made the big difference. A novel advertising campaign was launched in which people were made to anxiously await the appearance, in America, of more Camels than there were in Europe. This new blend with its modern advertising campaign, in the words of the U. S. Supreme Court "revolutionized the cigarette industry."

Cameron, Alexander

One of the largest American tobacco manufacturers of the post-Civil War era, Cameron belonged to a family that operated the largest tobacco enterprise of the United States up to the time of the formation of the American Tobacco Co.

Campana

The tuck, or opened end, of the cigar; the end that is lit.

Can

Slang for a half pound of smoking tobacco.

Canada

Tobacco has to some extent been grown in all Provinces of Canada, but it is chiefly produced in Ontario (flue-cured, Burley, fire-cured and dark air-cured types) and in Quebec (cigar leaf and smoking tobacco types). Simcoe, Ontario, has become the marketing centre for tobacco used in the production of Canadian cigarettes. Though the industry is comparatively recent—it was virtually begun in 1932—the estimated production of bright flue-cured tobaccos alone should, in 1954, run some seventy million dollars.

Canasta

(Basket). The shallow woven basket in which leaves are carried from Cuban tobacco fields to the factories.

C (a) naster (Kanaster, etc.)

A highly desirable fragrant tobacco imported into Europe from Venezuela and neighboring lands. Its name is from the

Spanish, *canastro, canasto*: large (rush) basket, in which twist tobacco was packed, and in which form this tobacco, C (a) naster—was imported.

Cancer of the Lung

At various times tobacco in one form or another has been regarded as either a cause of disease or a cure. Some 300 diseases have been attributed to tobacco. The most serious charge is that cancer of the lung is caused by excessive cigarette smoking. Beginning around 1923 scientific reports have appeared purporting to show a relationship between the two. The statistical evidence runs as follows: In this country in 1933 there were 100 billion cigarettes smoked and 3,400 deaths from lung cancer; in 1953 about 400 billion cigarettes and 22,000 lung cancer deaths. Experiments with mice, notably by painting their backs with tobacco tars or by subjecting them to cigarette smoke, were successful in inducing cancer. In the former case, Dr. Evert Graham and Dr. Ernest Wynder had sensational results. In 1951 Professor E. Cuyler Hammond began directing an extensive study for the American Cancer Society of the smoking habits of 204,000 living males and their possible connection with lung cancer. In 1953 there was a decline of 2% in cigarette consumption in this country, the first falling off in more than twenty years. Late in the year there was a precipitate drop in tobacco company stocks. Several of the major cigarette companies promptly set up a tobacco Industry Research Committee to study all phases of tobacco use and health in hopes of disproving the lung cancer theory, or if not, to isolate the offending ingredient in tobacco and find ways of eliminating it. In January 1954 Dr. Anthony I. Lanza, New York University Professor of Cancerology, asserted that "scientific investigation is in less than the embryonic state and lung cancer statistics show little."

Cane

Sixteenth-seventeenth century English term applied to pure tobacco leaf, especially in an unshredded package form, a slender roll in which it was sold by the apothecaries.

see also CARACAS AND PUDDING

Canon

(Tube). The body of a Cuban cigar, referring especially to its shape. Straight cigars are called *cañon parejo*, tapering cigars *cañon ahuevado*, and pointed cigars *cañon figurado*.

Capa

The wrapper of a Cuban cigar. Wrapper leaves are called *Caperos*. Wrappers are classified as *Capa Clara* or light, and *Capa Madura* or dark; *Capa de la tripa*, second-grade wrappers made from filler leaves, and *Capaduras*, wrappers made from second crop leaves or suckers.

Capaduras

Choice (first or second) grades of tobaccos grown in the Remedios section of Cuba.

Caraccas (Caracas)

Applied to tobacco from Venezuela and neighboring lands. Also known as cane.

Carolina Bright

A flue-cured hybrid of Four Hundred and Gold Dollar. Its broad leaves are spaced medium close on the stalk, which is large. When cured they are a bright lemon color.

Carot of Perique

In the late eighteenth century the best medium of exchange in Louisiana was the "carot" of tobacco. These had definite weight and value. They were sometimes prepared in the same manner as frontier plug (*see* PLUG TOBACCO). Snuff was made by grating tobacco from the end of a carot and was used by both men and women of that time.

Carotte

A tobacco popular in France in the early seventeenth century. A sweet leaf, it was formed in long thin rolls, flavored with treacle, cut like modern pigtail.

Carr, Julian Shakespeare (1845-1924)

Partner of William T. Blackwell, he helped make the Bull Durham Factory the largest tobacco factory in the world in the nineteenth century.

Carroll, John W. (1832-1898)
Founder of one of the so-called "Lynchburg Pipe mixtures" known as "Lone-Jack."

Carrot (manojo)
In Cuban industries a carrot is composed of four hands of tobacco leaves tied together with raffia-bast or guana fiber. Eighty carrots make a bale.

Cartabon
The mold used in the Cuban cigar industry, especially the mold used to shape the filler in the poorer cigars made by the boncheros.

Carter, Robert (1663-1732)
He was the richest and most famous of the tobacco planters. He held many offices during his lifetime such as: Colonial Treas., member of the House of Burgesses, Speaker of the House, President of the Council etc. . . . At the time of his death in 1732, he possessed 700 slaves and 300,000 acres of land.

Case (Kase)
1) Cured cigar tobaccos which are in safe keeping order are in "case." When too wet are said to be in "high case."

2) A specified amount of cigar tobacco packed into a wooden case in the warehouse where it is fermented. A case of tobacco usually weighs about four hundred pounds.

3) In a cigar-manufacturing plant a case of tobacco received from the grower is resized, dipped, and recased for another period of fermentation, usually about six months.

The case of tobacco in the manufacturer's warehouse generally weighs about three hundred and thirty-five pounds.

4) The term is also used synonymously with "ordering."

Cash
An early-maturing variety of flue-cured tobacco. The plant grows fairly tall, and the leaves are quite widely spaced on the stalk. They have small fibers and considerable body and usually cure to an orange color. This variety is grown chiefly on medium to fertile soils.

Casing

Applying flavoring hydroscopic agent, etc., on blending strips before cutting.

Castaway

Cigar or cigarette stub (slang).

Catcher

The operator who places the newly made cigarettes coming out of the cigarette-making machine on a tray preparatory for inspection. Cigarettes come from the machine on a conveyor belt called the catcher belt.

Caterinaire

see HERBE DE LA REINE

Catorcena

(Fourteenth). The classification for Cuban filler leaves with defects and clean wrapper leaves of the Vuelta Abajo district.

Cavalla

The chief town and port in Macedonia, opposite Thesos. It was at Thesos, then called Neopolis, that St. Paul landed on his way to Philippi. Macedonian tobacco raised in this region is frequently called Cavalla tobacco, though Cavalla is not the proper name for any type of Turkish tobacco.

Cavendish

1) Sweetened, manufactured tobacco products. In the best sense of the term, it applies to Virginia leaf which has been darkened by resweating, placed in molds and pressed in bars or cakes. It is then cut into flake, granulated, etc.

2) Any type of tobacco which has been dipped into sweetening (sugar-water, rum, maple syrup, etc.). Generally a dark brown or mahogany colored leaf. Named for Captain Cavendish, whose famous voyage helped bring tobacco to England.

Cecil soils

A series of soils especially favorable to the growth of dark-fired tobaccos. Cecil clays and Cecil sandy loams are characterized by a heavy red clay subsoil. Cecil sandy loams have a grey gravelly topsoil and are known locally as "gray soils."

Cellar

Baled tobacco, especially of the air-cured varieties, is often stored in warehouse cellars.

Cellar Mold

Baled tobacco which has been allowed to remain too long in the cellar is apt to become moldy from the dampness.

Celtic pipe

see FAIRY PIPE

Centros

Middle leaves of the Cuban tobacco plant. These are the best leaves.

Chain smoking

Smoking one cigarette after another by lighting a fresh cigarette from the one just smoked. (Slang).

Chakka

see LAYING A CHAKKA

Charge or Charger

Extension used on top of hogshead when filled with leaf tobacco in leaf processing plants.

Charket

Briquetted charcoal used in tobacco barns.

Chaveta

The Cuban term for the knife used by a cigar-maker to cut the wrapper and shape the tip of the cigar.

Chaw

Corruption of "chew" generally referring, in this country, to plug, but the term is not local. On the 7th of June, 1665, Samuel Pepys bought "some roll tobacco, to smell to, and chaw . . ."

Cheese

The pressurized mass entering the mouthpiece of the cigarette cutting machine.

Cheroot

A cigar of simple construction and, usually, small size, open at both ends and made of tobaccos not commonly used in standard cigars. Frequently made without a binder.

Chesterfields

This cigarette—a creation of Liggett and Myers—first appeared in 1912. It was a usual blend of domestic tobaccos. However, due to the innovations of R. J. Reynolds, with their Camels, the Chesterfields were changed to fit the pattern, so that by 1917, it became one of the standard brands together with Camels and Lucky Strikes.

Chilcagre

A type of tobacco grown in Nicaragua.

Chimo

A thick tarry dark paste prepared and used in Venezuela, made by evaporating the water from boiled ripened leaves and suckers. The residue is sold in containers. A small ball is placed in the mouth of the user in the same manner as in dipping snuff.

China

Tobacco was introduced into southern coastal ports by the Portuguese. Trade with the Spanish-held Philippines provided a steady source of supply, and the herb gradually became accepted throughout the interior as well as the southern regions. Later, tobacco became almost as much a part of Chinese social life as tea. Northern China and Manchuria received the herb from Japan, through Korea, and accepted the habit at about the same time. The last ruler of the Ming dynasty attempted, in 1641, to prohibit the use of tobacco, but the effort proved futile, and smoking met with no further opposition in China.

In 1949 China raised 16.7% of the world's tobacco. Tobacco is grown in nearly all provinces of China on a wide range of soil and climatic conditions. It is almost entirely used for domestic consumption.

Chisel-Injection

A method of soil fumigation wherein the liquid chemical is applied in bands about ten inches apart and six to eight inches deep. The gas given off by the liquid permeates through the cultivated soil, insuring an even treatment.

Chloropicrin

(Larvacide or tear gas), an effective nematicide, fungicide and bactericide applied in the fall when the soil temperature is between 55° and 70° F. A hand injector is used, making injections about 10 inches apart.

Chocolate Soils

Cecil clays which have a heavy red clay subsoil and a heavy red topsoil.

Chohobba

see COHOBA

Churchwarden

A long-stemmed pipe, usually of clay, of English origin, a descendant of the long clay pipes used during the seventeenth century. The bowl of such pipes is set at a slight forward angle. The pipe may be distinguished not only by its unusually long stem—often twelve inches or more—but by a small knob or solid extension at the base of the bowl, the portion of the pipe which extended from the mold in which the clay was poured.

Chute Selling

In the central market towns of western Kentucky it was for awhile a common practice to drive wagons of tobacco down a chute or driveway so that it could be examined by the buyers, who stood on a platform beside the "chute."

Cigar

Any tubular construction of tobacco leaf in which the filler or body is wrapped in tobacco leaf. Cigars are of three parts, the filler, the binder and the wrapper. In principle these leaves come from the upper, middle and lower parts of the same plant respectively. Normally, however, the several classes of tobaccos are especially raised for one purpose only.

The cigar industry is much older than the cigarette industry but reached a maximum production about two decades ago. From earliest times Cuba has been outstanding in the growing of fine cigar leaf. The leaf for the majority of domestic cigars is, however, produced in this country. Superior cigars are made from "long filler," cheaper items from "short filler" or "scrap." For the latter, domestic leaf grown in Pennsylvania and Ohio is usually used: for medium-priced cigars a combination of Puerto-Rican and Cuban filler leaf with Connecticut Broadleaf or Seedleaf wrappers. Higher priced "Clear-Havana" cigars are frequently produced in this country but contain only Cuban filler, binder and wrapper. "Genuine Havanas" are hand made in Cuba entirely of Havana tobacco. Originally all cigars were made by hand, but, since 1902, machines have taken over more and more of the manufacturing processes. Nearly all domestic cigars are machine-made.

Cigar Binder Types

These are produced in the Connecticut Valley and Wisconsin. They are graded as class five by the Department of Agriculture of the United States Government.

Cigar Filler Types

The Department of Agriculture of the United States has graded as class four the cigar-filler Types. These include the Pennsylvania seedleaf which is grown in Lancaster County, Pa., as well as certain types cultivated in the Miami Valley of Ohio. One also finds Puerto Rican filler graded in the same way.

Cigar Institute of America

A national association dedicated to the advancement of trade relations and consumer acceptance of cigars; that is, to encourage and expand consumption of cigars in the United States.

Cigar Manufacturers Association of the U. S.

A national organization which represents cigar manufacturers in their dealings with the government in matters on taxation, labour and fair trade practices.

Cigar tobaccos

The bulk of the cigar-tobacco crop is grown in Massachusetts, Connecticut, New York, Pennsylvania, Wisconsin, Ohio, Florida and Georgia. The finest grades of domestic wrapper leaf are raised in the Connecticut Valley and in a few counties of western Florida and southern Georgia. Wisconsin is known as a binder state. New York, Pennsylvania and Ohio produce mainly filler grades. Except for wrapper types, where some artificial heat may be applied, all cigar tobaccos are air-cured. The finest cigar tobaccos are grown in Cuba in the Vuelta Abajo region.

Cigar Wrapper Types

The two most expensive domestic types of produce are the Connecticut Valley shade-grown and the Georgia and Florida shade-grown. These are graded class six by the Department of Agriculture of the United States Government.

Cigarette

Any filler of finely cut tobaccos rolled in paper may be termed a cigarette, but excluding the hand-rolled variety, cigarettes have become one of the most familiar and highly specialized products of modern times. Manufactured cigarettes are classified as large, weighing more than three pounds per thousand, and small, weighing less than three pounds per thousand. The small cigarette is just over an inch in circumference and two and eight-tenths inches long. A thousand such cigarettes contain just over two pounds moisture-free blended tobacco composed chiefly of flue-cured varieties with small amounts of Burley, Maryland and Turkish leaf added according to the manufacturer's formula. The cigarette industry, which produced over one hundred and eighty-nine billion small cigarettes in 1940, is highly mechanized, and nearly all stages of the manufacturing process are standardized. The machines which form the finished cigarette are capable of producing a thousand cigarettes a minute. Packaging of the cigarettes is likewise done automatically. The first cigarette machine, invented in 1872, was perfected a few years later. Production of cigarettes at that time averaged less than fifty millions a year. Since 1900 per capita use of cigarettes has increased steadily, the greatest boost coming in the period between 1940 and 1945.

Cigarette Beetle

see TOBACCO BEETLE

Cigarette Paper

see RICE PAPER

Cigarillo

Trade name for a very small thin cigar with a straight-cut tuck end.

Cigarro

In Cuba, any cigarette is called Cigarro, but in some other Spanish-speaking countries, the term applies to cigars, especially to cigars made by twisting filler within a binder which serves also as a wrapper.

Circuit Walker

The head buyer who supervises the buying of green tobacco in a particular market.

Civil War - U.S.

During the Civil War of the United States, the tobacco region split. Maryland, Missouri and Kentucky joined the Confederate States. Thus neither side—the North and the South—suffered any tobacco shortage during the conflict.

Clarksville Fire-cured

Common name for one of the fire-cured tobaccos produced principally in a section east of the Tennessee River, in southern Kentucky and northern Tennessee. Government classified as Type 22 of Class 2.

Claro

(Light). Cuban wrapper leaf of a light color, selected by the "Rezagador" (which see). This is the second color grade, *Caro Pajizo* (Light Straw) being the lightest.

In Puerto Rican tobaccos, *Claro* indicates the lightest color.

Class

One of the major divisions of leaf tobacco based on the distinct characteristics of the tobacco caused by differences in varieties, soil, and climatic conditions, and the methods of handling, cultivation and curing.

Tobaccos of the same type belong to a common class. These are assigned by government authority. Class 1 includes all flue-cured types; Class 2, fire-cured types; Class 3, air-cured; Class 4, cigar filler types; Class 5, cigar binder; Class 6, cigar wrapper; Class 7, miscellaneous types; Class 8, foreign types.

see TOBACCO

Classer

In flue-cured regions one who examines bundles of leaves from the opened hogs-head and classifies each bundle into more than half dark or more than half light leaves.

Clay

A clay pipe (colloquial).

A common, grayish-white, earthy, highly plastic material used by North American Indians and adopted by the English and other Europeans in the 17th century for the making of tobacco pipes. Clays are still being manufactured.

Clean

1) In reference to tobacco, freedom from foreign matter.

2) In reference to soil, fumigated land.

Clear Havana

Cigars made entirely of imported Havana tobacco but produced in this country. Also termed all-Havana cigars.

Clergy

From early days of the settlement the services of the clergy in Virginia were paid for in tobacco. (This also applied to Maryland and some other Southern colonies). By the early 18th century Virginia clergymen received 16 thousand pounds of tobacco annually as salary, the equivalent of about £ 80. When tobacco was scarce because of drought a Virginia law in 1755 allowed payment in money or tobacco and in 1758 allowed tobacco to be paid at twopence the pound. The clergy protested and a famous case, generally known as the Parsons' Cause, followed. Patrick Henry defended the taxpayers against the clergy and won the suit.

see Parsons' Cause

Clincher

Underworld slang for a cigarette clinched between finger tips and extinguished so that it may be smoked again. The term is most current in prison life.

Clip a Butt

American underworld slang for putting out a partially burned cigarette in order to save it for future smoking.

Clip-Board

A board like an artist's palette on which the clip-man makes out tickets.

Clip-Man

The clerk who makes out a statement covering the lot sold by each grower.

Club

A style of pipe with a rather long somewhat oval shank and a very short stem. The bowl is round.

Club-root

A rare tobacco disease, cause unknown. Succeeding leaves on the afflicted plant tend to grow progressively shorter, and to stand out at right-angles from the stalk. The plant may acquire a pyramidal shape. The roots of infected plants become enlarged.

Coal

Sixteenth and seventeenth century tobacco pipes were lit by means of a live coal or ember, usually of juniper wood, held over the bowl.

Coddle

Colloquial term peculiar to flue-cured areas in Virginia indicating wilt resulting from too much heat from the sun.

Coffin Nail

A cigarette (slang).

Cohoba

A powder used in Haiti and South America by natives who inhaled it through the nose. Evidence indicates that this powder was tobacco. The prevalence of tobacco among the West Indians and the ritualistic significance of Cohoba give rise to this impression. The method of using Cohoba varied. In South America it was placed in the center bowl of a four-tubed instrument designed to be used by two persons. By blowing through the lower tube (which was placed in the mouth) each person might drive a small quantity of the tobacco into the upper tube inserted in his companion's nostril. Tobacco was for many years known by this name in the West Indies.

Col-Claro or Colorado-Claro

A Puerto Rican cigar leaf of light-medium or good coloring.

College of William and Mary

When established, this institution received as part of its total grant, the right to receive the income from the so-called "One Penny Tax of 1673," whereby all tobacco exported from Virginia or Maryland to another colony was taxed one penny per pound. The income from this tax was used to enable the youth of Maryland to attend the college. In this way tobacco was first used for the sake of education.

Color

The desirable quality in tobacco. The term has also a technical meaning; viz, a subdivision of a group based on the relative hues, saturations, and brilliances common to the group and on certain other elements of quality closely related to the color of the leaf.

In flue-cured tobaccos, the most desirable colors are, in order of preference, lemon, orange, red, dark red, and green.

Color Setting Stage

This is the second phase of curing flue-cured tobacco. It is preceded by the yellowing period and followed by the stem-drying phase.

Colorado

A cigar of medium coloring.

Colorado-Maduro

1) In Puerto Rican industry, a cigar of dark to medium coloring.

2) In Cuban industry, a cigar or leaf of dark red coloring.

Coloring

The first stage of curing flue-cured tobaccos, during which time the temperature is held at eighty to ninety degrees Fahrenheit under conditions of high relative humidity and little ventilation. This stage precedes the "fix," or "fixing the color," which see.

Colory

The British term for Yellow (air-cured) tobaccos.

Common tobacco

The name by which *Nicotiana rustica* is occasionally called in England, being a fairly common garden perennial.

Companie d'Occident

A company formed during the early part of the seventeenth century to provide France with an independent source of tobacco. M. de Montplaisir brought thirty colonists to the Natchez region on the Mississippi in order to begin a tobacco industry there. By the middle of the next century the annual export reached several hundred hogsheads.

Comstock Spanish

A Havana Seed tobacco grown in Wisconsin chiefly for binder leaf. Originally introduced under this name, Havana Seed is, nevertheless, the original Wisconsin variety, and it is identical with Comstock Spanish.

Condenser

The part of a tobacco pipe inserted in the tenon and projecting into the shank for the purpose of condensing moisture, tars, nicotine or other impurities. Sometimes called Fitment or Extension in this country, Systems in France and England.

Condition

A term used synonymously with *Case*. Tobacco which is in condition, or in case, is cured and has the right amount of moisture content to insure safe handling. The term is occasionally used as a verb indicating the later (fixative) stages of the curing process.

see CASE

Conditioning Chamber

Cigarette tobacco taken from the ordering machine is placed in hogsheads for aging. On removal it goes directly to the conditioning chamber where, by a scientific process, it is vacuum treated, then uniformly moistened.

Cigar tobacco is also conditioned by dampening the butt ends of the leaves with a heavy spray and the leaves with a light spray. After conditioning it remains for a period of forty-eight hours in cases so that it will be uniformly moist.

Connecticut Broadleaf
A domestic cigar-binder leaf raised in the Connecticut Valley sections of Connecticut and Massachusetts.

see BROADLEAF

Connecticut Tobaccos
The tobaccos grown mostly in Connecticut, in part of Massachusetts, and in a small portion of Vermont and New Hampshire: i.e., on lands immediately bordering on the Connecticut River, excepting the Housatonic Valley near New Milford. These tobaccos include Shadegrown, Broadleaf and Havana Seed, which are exclusively used in cigar manufacture.

Connecticut Valley Havana Seed
Common name for a cigar-binder tobacco raised principally in the Connecticut Valley. Government classified as Type 52. This type is also known as Primed Havana or Stalk-cut Havana.

Connecticut Valley Shade-grown
A domestic cigar wrapper leaf grown in the Connecticut Valley. Government classified as Type 61. Also known as Shade of Connecticut.

see SHADEGROWN

Cooking
When tobacco is kept in a forced sweat for more than four weeks without being shaken out, it "cooks"; that is, it becomes soft and mushy.

Cooler
Machine to remove heat from processed tobaccos.

Cooper
In the tobacco warehouse the person who assembles parts of a patented hogshead into usable form is called the cooper.

Copenhagen
see SWEDISH SNUFF

Corde (Cord)
Tobacco leaves formed into a thin rope.

see ROLL, PIGTAIL, PRICKE, TWIST

Corona
While there is some confusion about the term, it generally

applies to any "large" cigar which is cut squarely off at the tuck end. Cigar sizes and shapes vary greatly and at the whim of the individual manufacturer. Corona was originally a size marking for a popular clear-Havana cigar. The term simply meant "fine."

Coronas

In Cuban tobaccos, the top and upper leaves of the plant. *Corona Inferior* in the Puerto Rican tobaccos indicates choice heavy filler. The upper leaves of the plant generally being of a heavier quality than those from the middle, Coronas are used as fillers.

Counterblaste to Tobacco

An anti-tobacco tract written by James I of England in 1604. It claimed that the smoking habit resulted in laziness and questioned the medicinal value of the plant. It was published anonymously.

Cracus

see Caraccas or Caracas

Crane Fly

An insect which, in the larva stage, cuts the stem of seedlings of flue-cured tobaccos below the soil surface.

Cricket Moles

Common term for mole cricket in Southern coastal regions.

Crimp Cut

Smoking tobacco which has been cut in such a manner that individual pieces of leaf will curl slightly or maintain a wavy sometimes springy appearance. Naturally slow-burning tobaccos are usually crimp cut to ensure an even burn.

Criollo

The native, indigenous cigar tobacco of the Dominican Republic, a less choice variety than the Olor. Used mostly for domestic consumption and export to European countries.

Crooks

A cigar so molded as to form a kinky or crooked shape.

Crop

A term referring to certain domestic cigar tobaccos.
see Thin-crop

Crop-run
see PULL-OFF

Cropper
In Bright-leaf areas the term came to apply specifically to the tenant who furnished the labour, half the fertilizers and half the marketing costs.

Cropping
The term common throughout the flue-cured region for harvesting or for priming the tobacco plant.
see PRIMING

Crude
Unripe tobacco, generally characteristically green in colour. By government classification, any immature leaf more than one-fifth of which is definitely green; or, any lot of tobacco containing more than 30% crude leaves. Crude Cuban tobacco is termed *Crudo*.

Crumbs
North Carolina colloquialism for "trash."

Cry
After the Civil War inspectors employed by the warehouse or the farmer came to assume the tasks of the auctioneer, calling or "crying" out the quality and condition of their wares. Present day auctioneers may be referred to as "cryers."

Crystals
Trade term for cigars packaged in glass tubes which insure the proper humidity for the cigar and protect it from foreign odors. Only more expensive cigars are so packaged.

Cuban Blade
The knife used in making cigars. It is a flat blade about as wide as a man's hand, with no handle. In Cuba this is called *Chaveta*.

Cuban tobacco
Tobacco grown in Cuba. Tobacco was discovered on the eastern part of the Island, near Gibara, during Columbus' first voyage. The Cuban tobacco industry has become increas-

ingly important with the growing popularity of tobacco. Cuban cigars are considered to be the finest made.

see HAVANA

Cuban wrappers

see PARTIDOS AND VUELTA ABAJO

Cubeb

A berry which is dried unripe and used as medicine in bronchial and other diseases. Often smoked in the form of cigarettes. Medicated cigarettes sold under this name were popular around 1920.

Cucumber Mosaic

A tobacco disease similar in effect to mosaic, but different in that it is readily spread by aphids and that mosaic resistant varieties of tobacco are easily infected by it. Not as common as mosaic.

Cud

Colloquial variation of quid.

Cultivation

Any working of the soil between plants with horse or tractor drawn equipment. Loosening the soil.

Cure

The process of drying the sap from newly harvested tobacco. This is done either naturally, by using the sun, or by artificial means, such as flue-curing or fire-curing. In flue-cured regions this process includes the yellowing, the color-fixing and the leaf-drying stages. Curing is done in the barn especially constructed for this purpose, in such a manner as to permit air-curing, fire-curing or flue-curing.

Every tobacco has its own best method of curing.

Curve

A style of pipe characterized by a full-curved stem. That is, the shank rises almost vertically from the base of the pipe and the stem is so curved that the bit is at right angles to the top of the bowl. The bowl is round, the shank round and generally no longer than the bowl is high, and the stem is boldly curved.

Cut
Plug tobacco (slang).

Cut Filler
The resulting product after cutting strips for cigarettes. Also called rag.

Cut Havana
Cuban or Havana Seedleaf tobaccos cut into shreds or large flakes and blended for use in inexpensive long (normal-sized) cigars.

Cut plug
see PLUG

Cuts
British term for pipe or smoking tobaccos.

Cutter
1) One who harvests mature Burley tobacco by cutting the entire stalk off close to the ground and splitting the stalk so it will slip down on a stick.

2) Machine for shredding leaf tobacco into cut filler.

Cutters
1) In flue-cured tobacco, a group characterized by thin, spready leaves, medium in body as compared with the average type.

2) In flue-cured regions, leaves which grow a quarter to half the way up the plant are referred to as "cutters."

3) In Burley tobaccos the same characteristics as the cutters of flue-cured tobaccos apply, with the addition that the leaf has an open wave and a very light to fairly true color shade and is sufficiently strong to be stemmed into whole strips.

4) In Bright tobaccos, grades which are used mainly for cutting purposes; i.e., for making cigarettes.

see THIN-CROP AND LUGS

Cutting
In cigarette tobaccos, the process of cutting strips into shredded tobacco. With Broadleaf and Havana Seed tobaccos cutting refers to harvesting the crop and includes topping the plant, cutting the stalk and plant, spearing the stalk onto

the stick, and curing the leaf as it hangs by its stalk in the tobacco shed.

Cuttings

Small pieces of tobacco leaf which cigar manufacturers do not care to use.

see TUCKS

Cutty

A short Scottish pipe. Cutty is the Scotch word for short. The pipe might not be over three inches in length.

Cutworm

A common insect pest, some twenty species of which feed on the tobacco plant. Principal among these are the variegated cutworm, which attacks both the seedlings and the grown plant, the greasy cutworm, the clay-backed, the dingy, the spotted and the dark-sided cutworms. Control is generally handled through poison bait spread on the soil.

D

Dakka
The native name for hemp. Hemp smoking was common among the Hottentots and Bushmen tribes. Later pipes used for this purpose were frequently water-pipes, made by setting a wooden bowl on a gourd or bamboo stem which held the water.

Da-li-hse
A chopped or shredded pipe tobacco produced in Burma.

Damaged
By government classification, tobacco affected by mold, must, rot or other fungus or bacterial diseases which attack the cured leaf.

Damp
Farmers of the Connecticut Valley wait for a "damp," a fog or a rain (corresponding to the season in flue-cured areas) before removing the cured tobacco from the sheds.

Damp Tobacco
Tobacco of the air-cured variety which has been ordered too highly, which is in high case or when it has been too much dampened to insure its pliability. Also baled tobacco which has lain too long in a damp cellar and is subject to cellar mold.

Damping-off
A plant-bed disease caused by organisms present in most soils, affecting very young seedlings. The plants may dry up and disappear or may be shriveled by the fungus attack. More prevalent in damp areas and where organic fertilizers have been used to excess.

Also called Red Rot.

Dark-fired or Dark Fire-cured
A term used synonymously with fire-cured to indicate tobaccos which have been so cured.

DAKKA PIPE

An early *dakka* pipe, used for smoking hemp. Such a pipe
was the probable fore-runner of the East Indian *nargileh*.
The bowl was carved from wood and the stem made of
bamboo.

—Arents Tobacco Collection, New York Public Library.

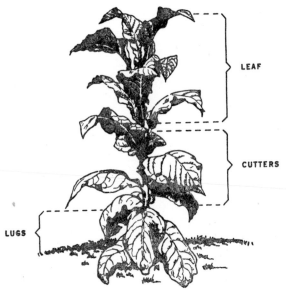

LEAF

CUTTERS

LUGS

FLUE-CURED TOBACCO PLANT

This figure shows the approximate stalk positions of the various grade groupings for flue-cured leaves. The most desirable leaves on the flue-cured plant are generally called "leaf" but may include many grades, depending upon the size, color and condition of the leaves themselves.

*—Production and Marketing Administration,
U. S. Department of Agriculture.*

Dark Fired is another name for Dark Virginia leaf.

Dark fire-cured tobaccos are used in the manufacture of snuff, plug or twist. A small amount is employed in the production of Italian-type cigars.

The primary classifications of this type of leaf are wrappers, thin leaf, heavy leaf and lugs.

Dark Shag

A form especially popular in Britain. Processed tobacco is molded into blocks or bars about an inch and a half thick. These are slightly baked before cutting. Cavendish is a form of dark shag tobacco.

Dark Snuff Grades

Dark grades, either fired or air-cured, heavy-bodied, and used for snuff.

Dark Tobacco District Planters' Protective Association

An association of farmers opposed to tobacco monopolists of the early twentieth century.

see NIGHT RIDERS

Dark Virginia

Common name for one of the fire-cured tobaccos raised principally in the Piedmont and mountain sections of Virginia. Government classified as Type 21 of Class 2.

Dark Virginia Air-cured

Common name for a type of air-cured tobacco produced principally in the central section of Virginia, north of the James River. Government classified as Type 37, Class 3.

Darks

A local term to designate second-grade Broadleaf and Havana Seed cigar tobaccos of the heavy binder type. Darks are not coarse, they are elastic to stretchy, very oily to fairly oily, fairly ripe, not stringy, and may be of a dark or dingy color.

In domestic Broadleaf darks are divided into two grades, Darks and No. 2 Darks.

Dawes

see GENERAL DAWES

D-D

A commercial preparation composed of *dichloropropene*

and *dichloropropane,* an effective control for nematodes.

Dead

Leaves, especially of the flue-cured types, which lack color or are dull or muddy in tone are said to be dead.

Dead Man, or Dead soldier

Cigar or cigarette stub (slang).

Decayed

Tobacco which, by government definition, is damaged to the extent of 20% or more.

Décimos

A box of one hundred Cuban cigars, or ten boxes to a case of a thousand cigars.

Deer's-tongue

An herb native to the South-eastern United States which provides a substitute for vanilla and a flavoring agent for tobacco, especially for pipe tobaccos.

Deli

Local term for Sumatra tobacco, a distinctive variety originally derived from Cuban strains. Deli is a district in the Province of East Sumatra Coast. Tobacco produced in this area and in the adjoining district of Langkat is unsurpassed as a cigar wrapper leaf. The natural conditions permit the growing of tobacco under similar circumstances to those imitated in the shade-growing regions of Connecticut. The majority of this crop is exported to this country.

de Mata

Puerto Rican term for stalk-cut stripper, or stripped wrapper leaves which have been cut from the stalk of the plant instead of primed.

Den

American underworld slang for the place where addicts may enjoy opium and other narcotics. In general slang usage the term usually includes the word opium; viz, the opium dens of Shanghai.

Desecho

Trash from all grades of rejected (cut) Cuban tobaccos. Also called *diecisietecena.*

Deshojado

Puerto Rican term meaning Primed Stripper, or stripped wrapper leaves which have been picked early in a shade-grown culture.

De Xeres, Rodrigo

The first person said to have smoked in Europe.

He learned the habit from the natives of Cuba when he went to that country as one of the members of Christopher Columbus' crew. It was at the time of Columbus' first voyage to the New World.

Dibble

The peg which was driven into the ground in order to insert the transplanted seedling more easily. Obviated by the tobacco setter and other machinery.

Dieciochocena

(Eighteenth). Cuban tobacco of the Vuelta Abajo district generally fitting the nondescript classification as to grade, but not scrap. In the Remedios area, called *Bote*.

Dieciseicena

(Sixteenth). A classification of Cuban tobacco from the Vuelta Abajo district including clean filler leaf used for better type cigars but too small for use as binders.

Diecisietecena

(Seventeenth). A classification of Cuban tobacco from the Vuelta Abajo district including smaller leaves than those of the *Dieciseicena* grades but which are satisfactory for fillers.

Dill, J. G.

Together with his brother Adolph, he created Dill's Best, plug and cut-plug.

Dinch, Dincher

A cigar or cigarette stub (slang).

Dip

1) The hydroscopic agent through which tobacco leaves are run, in flue-cured tobaccos generally glycerine, in order to moisten the cured leaf so that it can be handled without breaking. In cigar tobaccos a solution of water and wine is usually used. This heightens the natural changes brought

about through forced sweating but does not affect the flavour of the tobacco.

2) The very thin weak leaves which grow at the bottom of the Basma plant, a type of Turkish tobacco. Dip is not sold.

Dipping

1) The habit of dipping a short wet stick into the snuff-box in order to gather the tobacco dust in a convenient form. Dipping was popular in the middle of the nineteenth century and was especially popular among women of certain classes in the South.

2) As a general term, dipping snuffs are snuffs such as the so-called Scotch, Swedish, Polish and Copenhagen varieties, which are taken into the mouth, as opposed to French (inhaled) snuffs.

Direct Accounts

Accounts between cigarette manufacturers and jobbers. Also those jobbers who buy in direct accounts may be called direct accounts.

Direct List

The practice of selling tobacco directly to a list of customers without obliging them to buy through jobbers.

Disease

Any affliction of the tobacco leaf, except those from physical causes such as wind, storm, etc. The term includes damage by fungus or virus, chemical changes in the organic structure of the leaf, and unknown causes. The most important are Granville wilt, black root rot, blue mold, pole sweat, and mosaic, *which see.*

Divine herb

Tobacco was popularly called the divine herb in sixteenth and seventeenth century Europe. Its medicinal effect was, for some years, its chief interest in England, where it was sold exclusively in apothecary shops until about 1603.

Dixie Bright

Dixie Bright 27, 101 and 102 are hybrid varieties of flue-cured tobacco raised chiefly in North Carolina. They differ from one another in their resistance to disease and physical characteristics, such as height, shape of leaf, etc. The color of the cured leaves in all three cases is yellow.

Djebel

A Turkish tobacco used for blending purposes. Raised in Bulgaria, but in the same region and from the same seed as Xanthi, but differing in that it is distributed only from Bulgarian markets and under this name.

Djubek

A Russian tobacco used mostly for pipe smoking, grown on the south-east coast of the Crimea, near Yalta. The leaf is full-bodied, aromatic and strong, generally of a yellowish-orange color.

Doce

(Twelfth). A classification of shadegrown Cuban tobacco from the Vuelta Abajo district, including large wrapper leaves of good body and size.

Dock-Tobacco

This type of tobacco was derived from "dock," a coarse and weedy herb often used as a substitute for tobacco. It was sold as tobacco, or blended with tobacco, by unscrupulous London sellers during the sixteenth century.

Dodder

A parasitic flower plant generally found where Korean lespodeza has been grown. There it may so thickly infest the tobacco field as to destroy practically all of the plants.

Dope stick

A cigarette (slang).

Dottle

The unconsumed tobacco caked in a pipe bowl. Not to be confused with Heel.

Dowfume W-40

A commercial preparation composed of 20% Ethylene Dibromide, effective in controlling nematodes.

Downy mildew

Another term for blue mold.

Drag

Slang for drawing or inhaling, as "Gimme a drag of your

cigarette." In less polite quarters the expression is "cop a drag."

Drake, Sir Francis

Brought quantities of captured tobacco leaves and seeds, as well as Indian clay-pipes from the West Indies in 1573, and pipes and tobacco from "Virginia" and the West Indies in 1586. As a result not only was the development of smoking aided, but the pipe became a national institution of England.

Draw

1) In reference to a cigar, the draw indicates its burning qualities, whether it is slow or too fast burning, whether it burns evenly on all sides, etc.

2) In reference to cigarettes, mostly a slang expression synonymous with "inhale" but perhaps more polite than "drag."

Drawback

In British manufacturing, the duty paid on imported leaf does not legally apply to scrap and waste. Thus the manufacturer is allowed a carefully calculated return on the duty he has paid on all scrap accumulated during the manufacturing process. This is called drawback.

Drawing

After tobacco prepared for the cigarette industry is run through the dryer and cooler, it is lightly sprayed with flavoring, packed in boxes, and covered for twenty-four hours. During this time the flavoring penetrates all the leaves, and is then ready for the cigarette manufacturing machine. As the flavoring penetrates it is said to "draw," and the process is referred to as the "drawing."

see PULLING PLANTS

Draw Twist

A plan for hanging primed or cut tobacco whereby bundles of leaves were wrapped around the tobacco stick with a continuous piece of twine which was drawn and twisted.

Dream Stick

A cigarette (slang).

Dresser

Machine for fluffing and opening tobacco.

Drinking Tobacco

The term generally applied, in England during the early seventeenth century, to smoking, no doubt in reference to the popular habit of inhaling (and apparently swallowing) the smoke.

Drop Shipment

An order of tobacco may be sent directly from the manufacturer to the retailer, when it is so requested by the wholesale dealer. In this case the wholesaler not only assumes responsibility for the order but is billed for the shipment, which is called a "drop shipment."

Dropping

Distributing tobacco seedlings in their proper places along the rows in the field. The "dropper" is the person, machine or machine operator who lays the plants on the earth at regular intervals on the row so that they are ready for the planter.

Drought Spot

An injury to the leaves brought on by prolonged dry weather and producing Rim Fire.

Drowning

Plants which have stood in waterlogged soil for forty-eight hours or more generally die. The roots are asphyxiated and soon decay. When drowned plants wilt they are said to flop.

Drummer

The cigar salesman of the late nineteenth and early twentieth century who distributed with his cigars the many premiums then popular—pictures of actresses and prize fighters, matches, cigar cutters, etc.

Dry Smoke

An unlighted cigar, cigarette, or pipe held between the teeth (slang).

Dry Snuff

A general type of snuff prepared much in the same manner as is moist snuff, except that it is not scented. The resulting pulverized form is drier in texture and less aromatic than moist snuff. Welsh, Scotch and Irish snuffs are of the dry variety.

Dry Weather Crop

The weather conditions under which cigar tobaccos are raised greatly affect their handling later. Crops raised in dry weather (called Dry Weather Crops) can be used fifteen to eighteen months after harvest. Wet Weather Crops may not be used for two or more years.

Dry Weather Frenching

A common term for Mosaic, a virus disease, which see.

Drying

Process of drying strips after removal of stems.

Dubec

1) Sorted leaves of superior Turkish tobaccos, generally a blend of leaves belonging to the top four grades from the Basma plant.

2) Also a ballot of Basma tobacco.

Duckbill (cf Spoonbill)

A small hand truck used to move baskets of tobacco around the warehouse floor.

Ducked

Tobacco which had been spilled or damaged while in transport down the rivers on flat-bottom boats. Such tobacco was generally resold, and, in the early part of the nineteenth century, the term came to have a specific legal meaning in reference to damaged tobacco.

Dudeen

A very short Irish pipe, sometimes less than three inches long.

Duke, James Buchanan (1856-1925)

Member of the Duke family, he was noted for his modern approach to the tobacco-business, thru the use of large-scale capital, modern machinery, aggressive salesmanship, and monopolistic organization. Among his accomplishments was the introduction of cigarette manufacture, by the Dukes in 1881, which was instrumental in increasing the popularity of cigarette smoking with the American Public. Perhaps his most notable achievement was the formation of the American Tobacco Company out of several rival firms, in 1890. He is also remembered as a philanthropist, having been the creator of the Duke Endowment, which is used to aid colleges, churches, and hospitals.

He was one of the sons of Washington Duke, head of the famous Duke family, who, together with his sons, formed the firm, W. Duke & Sons, which eventually became the leading cigarette manufacturing company of its time. Eventually this firm, under the leadership of his son, James Buchanan Duke, became part of the American Tobacco Company.

Dull-crop
see HEAVY-CROP

Dull leaf
The top leaves of the plant grown in the Maryland region. Also called "second crop" to differentiate it from the "crop" or first priming of the "bright" or center leaves. Dull leaf tobacco is usually exported or used for making inexpensive cigar filler.

Dull Red
Dun Burley.
see DUN

Dump
Term applied to the rotating upending discharge apparatus in cigarette-making.

Dun
Tobacco chiefly composed of dull leaves. In Burley tobaccos such leaves are characteristically dark brown and are also called Dull Red. In Flue-cured tobaccos the same color is called Walnut.

Durham Bull
A trademark adopted by John Ruffin Green for his tobacco since he lived in Durham.

Dust
Pulverized scrap produced in the manufacture of cigars.

Dust is used only for fertilizer and in the manufacture of chemical compounds.

Dust

Tobacco for a pipe or cigarette (slang).

Dust Zone

The depth to which dust is able to permeate in surface broadcasting; i.e., in spreading dry fertilizers, etc., on the top of the surface.

Dutch

Common name for a cigar-filler tobacco raised in the Miami Valley section of Ohio, originally introduced from Germany about 1870. Government classified as type 43. Leaf of this type is also known as Shoestring Dutch or Little Dutch.

Dutch wine pipe

A porcelain pipe with a second or lower bowl beneath the tobacco chamber. The latter is filled with wine and the smoke drawn through this portion and through the long, often elegantly carved wood stem. The mouthpiece being curved at right angles to the stem, the pipe drops vertically from the smoker's mouth and is generally long enough so that it may be comfortably supported by the hand at chest-height. The wine pipe was usually delicately painted and frequently showed an unusual amount of artistic care in its creation.

Dwarf Tobacco

A 17th century term for a small variety of *Nicotiana rustica*.

Dynamite

A type of homemade snuff (slang).

E

Eastern District Bright

Also called Eastern Carolina Bright. Common name for one of the flue-cured tobaccos raised principally in the coastal section of North Carolina, north of the South River. Government classified as Type 12 of Class 1.

Eastern District Fire-cured

Common name for one of the fire-cured tobaccos produced principally in a section east of the Tennessee River, in southern Kentucky and northern Tennessee. Government classified as Type 22 of Class 2.

Eastern Fire-cured

Common name for one of the fire-cured tobaccos produced principally in the Piedmont and mountain sections of Virginia. Government classified as Type 21 of Class 2.

Eastern Flue-cured

Common name for one of the flue-cured tobaccos raised principally in the coastal section of North Carolina, north of the South River. Classified by government standards as Type 12 of Class 1.

Ebauchon

see STUMMEL

Ecume de Mer

French meerschaum, as the name sea foam indicates.

E Dees

A slang expression of the Colonial period indicating high praise, referring especially to the "Sweet Scented" tobacco of the Maryland region raised along the York and James rivers. Edward Digges' property on the York brought the best prices in the English markets. Originally the term referred to tobacco raised on his land.

E-hse

A tobacco used for making exported Burmese cheroots.

Elaborado Privado

A Cuban cigar maker who works in his own home, usually assisted by other members of his family. Genuine Havanas are frequently made by an *Elaborado Privado*.

Elfin Pipe

see FAIRY PIPE

Elizabeth I, Queen (1533-1603)

According to rumors, Sir Walter Raleigh taught the women of the Elizabethan Court to smoke. Once, when he allowed the Queen to take a few puffs, she grew upset with nausea, and it was thought that he poisoned her. But she recovered and is said to have required her ladies in waiting to smoke.

Embosser

An employee of a manufacturer who perforates with an embossing machine the weight and price shown on each pile of tobacco his company has bought.

England

As England came into her period of colonial expansion, her sailors followed the footsteps of Portuguese and Italians who had already begun to trade with the New World. Tobacco seeds were introduced into the British Isles through Portugal and France, and the plant aroused from the first a good deal of curiosity. Sir Walter Raleigh, who had brought several native Indians back to England with him, kept a plentiful source of the herb and himself smoked. Remnants of the ill-starred Virginia settlement likewise, upon returning to their native land, brought the custom spread quickly in London. By the end of Elizabeth's reign pipe smoking was usual throughout most of England. It was considered a proper gentlemanly accomplishment, the more so since tobacco at that time was literally worth its weight in silver and therefore beyond the price range of humbler folk.

James I, disliking tobacco, very soon took steps to discourage its use. Upon his accession to the throne he published a tract on the subject which pointed out that the heathen Indians used the weed as a cure against syphilis. Why, James demanded, didn't Englishmen walk naked and deny God as well as smoke tobacco as the natives did? The libel, however, made little difference. Superficial conformity to the King's views did not impede the progress of the tobacco trade.

The Virginia Colony, struggling again into existence, found tobacco its most lucrative crop. It paid for ninety marriageable English maids with tobacco at £150 a head and in the same year (1620) sent forty thousand pounds to the mother country. About the same time a new and powerful guild, the pipe-makers, applied for rights to carry on their trade, and James, taking a leaf from the French book, made tobacco a royal monopoly in order to control its growth, discourage its use and profit from the revenue which accrued. He prohibited the sowing of tobacco seed in his kingdom, but such decrees were not effective in curbing the smoking habit. Charles, succeeding in 1625, enforced James' monopoly, but allowed the importation of foreign tobaccos in order to increase the royal revenue, though still officially discouraging its use. When that unfortunate monarch finally met with his unhappy fate it is said that the soldiers blew smoke in his face and threw broken pipes in his path as he passed.

With the return of the monarchy in 1660 Charles II's courtiers brought from their exile in France the gentlemanly art of snuff dipping, and snuff taking continued to be popular well after the reign of Queen Anne. Cigars were introduced about 1829, and cigarettes in the 1860's. Tobacco continues to play an important part in England's economy today, though the plant is at present but little raised on the Island.

English tobacco

The *Nicotiana rustica* plant, which is not uncommon in English gardens, flowering from midsummer to Michaelmas.

(*see also* Henbane, yellow)

Enmatulado

A bale of Cuban tobacco.

Enumerated Articles

Due to violations of the Navigation Acts by the colonies, the British restricted the export of certain so-called "enumerated articles" to England and its dominions. Since tobacco was one of the "enumerated articles," a depression resulted in those areas growing it.

Erba Santa Croce

The name by which tobacco was known in Italy in the latter sixteenth century. The court of Italy had received a gift of tobacco plants from Cardinal Prospero di Santa Croce, who had obtained them in Portugal, and named the tobacco in his honor.

Erba Tornabuona

Since Nicolo Tornabuoni was thought to have introduced *Nicotiana Tabacum* into Italy, it was therefore named *Erba Tornabuona* in his honor and was so known during the sixteenth century.

Escogedor

A sorter in a Cuban tobacco factory.

Etch

A virus disease attacking tobacco plants, first seen in spots on the tip leaves, later in mottling of the leaves lower down. Differs from mosaic in that the tip leaves are not mottled. Is spread by aphids and present in most tobacco areas.

Etrenne

Probably the most popular of the snuffs annually presented to Louis XV by the French manufacturers.

Excise Factory

One division of tobacco manufacturing factory in England, as distinguished from the Bonded factory. In the Excise factory all duties are paid on the tobacco before it enters. The premises of the factory must also satisfy the requirements of the Excise.

Export

see MARYLAND AIR-CURED

Extension

see CONDENSER

F

Factory seconds or throw outs

Trade terms for cigars of high-grade tobacco but with slight color variations or slight imperfections which do not interfere with smoking enjoyment but which make them unsalable at the regular prices and cause them to be advertised at substantially lower prices.

Fag

A cigarette (Colloquial, Originally, British Slang).

Fag Drag

A cigarette smoke (slang).

Fairy Pipe of Ireland

A small clay pipe of the Elizabethan period which, it was claimed, had a fairy origin. Such pipes were dug up in various parts of England and Ireland. The bowl of early Elizabethan pipes was hardly more than an inch deep and a quarter of an inch in diameter. At one time there were attempts to prove pipe smoking of an earlier history than the introduction of tobacco from America. Fairy pipes were also called Celtic or Elfin pipes, depending on whether the natives wished to believe that smoking had originated in Ireland or Scotland.

Fallow

The local term for the most desirable color in Sumatra cigar wrapper leaf—that is, a grayish-brown. The Dutch term "vaal" gives us the color grade mark "V."

Farm Fillers

Inferior or badly injured leaves of the Pennsylvania Seed-leaf type, generally under 16" in length and from the lower part of the plant.

Farmer Buyer

The farmer employed by a merchant as a buyer. This practice is more common among air-cured tobacco dealers.

Farmer's Packings
Undersized and untied sorting leaf, specifically of cigar tobacco types.

Faroles
Literally, humbugs. Cigarettes which are defective or broken in manufacture.

Fast Burners
A prison slang expression for cigarettes which have been used too long as a medium of exchange and have become stale and burn too fast.

Fauma
A Cuban term meaning, literally, "to smoke." It has, however, come to have three specific meanings: 1. The name of a certain type of cigar. 2. The leaf which the planter keeps for his personal use, and 3. Cigars allotted to the cigar makers in Cuban factories where they work.

Feeling the Poles
Judging the temperature of flue-curing tobacco by touching or "feeling" the leaf on the lower poles in the curing barn.

Female petum
see PETUM FEMELLE

Female Tobacco
see PETUM FEMELLE

Ferbam
The active chemical in Fermate, Nuleaf or Ferradow, a chemical specific for the control of blue mold in flue-cured tobaccos.

Fermate
A chemical preparation (*ferric dimethyl dithiocarbamate*) used to control insects and blue mold.

Fermentation
All tobacco must be fermented or the taste is bitter and unpalatable and the aroma biting and pungent. The process removes the chemical constituents that produce these bad effects and permits the development of compounds producing a desirable taste and aroma.

see SWEATING

Ferradow

The common name for a chemical preparation used in insect control, especially in the flue-cured tobacco areas.

Ferrule

A band or ring around the shank of a tobacco pipe mainly to give it structural support.

Fertilization

The elements necessary to the effective growth of the tobacco plant vary considerably with soil conditions and plant types. Thus, while cigar tobaccos usually demand liberal fertilization, cigarette tobaccos are fertilized only to supply specific lacks in the soil on which they are raised. Farm manure, used in some areas, may encourage disease or otherwise harm development in another area. Chemical preparations are most customarily used, but generally in moderate amounts applied in the tobacco row.

Fighting Brands

Brands of tobacco sold at a loss or given away in order to undercut competing companies. Tactics such as the introduction of fighting brands were concomitant with the rise of big business methods during the 1880's.

Fill a Blanket

Prison slang for furnishing enough loose tobacco for "makin's" or hand-rolled cigarettes.

Filled Blankets

Rolled cigarettes (slang).

Filler

1) A term used specifically in cigar manufacture to indicate the core or inner part of the cigar which is encased in the binder and wrapper. Cigar-filler tobacco is tobacco which is used for this purpose. "Long fillers" are made of leaves which have been folded together and which run the entire length of the cigar. "Short fillers" are composed of scrap and small broken leaves.

2) In the cigarette industry, the cut tobacco or tobacco which has gone through the cutting machine is called the filler.

3) In Lancaster County the local term applied to the lower leaves of the plant and any damaged leaves from the middle or upper plant. These are commonly sold for scrap chewing and smoking tobaccos.

Fillers
see HEAVY-CROP

Fillin's
Slang for pipe or cigarette tobacco.

Filter
Any porous substance such as paper, cotton, cork, silicate jelly, meerschaum, etc., attached to the smoking end of a cigar or cigarette, or between the mouth and burning part of the tobacco in a pipe, to absorb moisture, tars, nicotine or other impurities. Also, such a substance contained in a separate holder in which a cigar or cigarette is inserted. Incorrectly called an aluminum System or Fitment.

Fine-cut
Chewing or smoking tobaccos, usually of Burley, Green River or fire-cured leaf, which is finely shredded—even finer, in some cases, than cigarette tobaccos.

Fino
One of the classifications used in grading Cuban tobacco, indicating fine or delicate leaves, usually with a bright color and silky appearance. Thus *Catorcena Fino* indicates one of the grades of clean wrapper leaves of the Vuelta Abajo district, a grade both light in color and thin in texture.

Fire
1) Tobacco which turns yellow in the field before it is ready for curing is said to fire.

2) To cure leaf by means of a fire, as in fire-cured tobaccos.

3) To dry over-moist leaf by means of a fire.

Fire-cured
Types of tobacco cured by means of an open fire, grown almost exclusively in western Kentucky and Tennessee and in central Virginia. Their principal characteristics are their dark color, heavy body, and a distinctive flavour imparted to them by the smoke of the open fires used in curing. The

greater portion of these types is exported or is used for the production of snuff and plug wrapper. Fire-cured tobaccos, as opposed to flue-cured and air-cured, are grown on heavy loam soils which contain a high percentage of clay or silt.

Tobacco of these types, produced mainly for export, is one of the oldest types of leaf-tobacco. It is used domestically for making smoking and chewing tobacco as well as snuff. It consists of a dark leaf which is rich in nicotine and has a very smoky odor. It is grown in Kentucky, Tennessee, and Virginia. The production of Fire Cured Tobacco is on the decline. It is graded as class two by the Department of Agriculture of the United States Government.

Fire-cured tobaccos include four types: Virginia (type 21), Kentucky-Tennessee, eastern district (22), Kentucky-Tennessee, western district (23), and Henderson, Stemming or North Fire-cured (24).

Fire Curing

This ancient method, which dates all the way back to pre-Columbian times, consists of drying the tobacco leaves in smoke.

Firming

Tamping the soil immediately after seeding.

First-crop

see THIN-CROP

Fitment

see CONDENSER

Fitzhugh, William

One of the prominent members of the planter-class of the Chesapeake Bay region. He was a member of the House of Burgesses, of the County Court and commander of the local-militia. At the time of his death he owned 54,000 acres and over fifty slaves.

Five-pack

Trade term for a package of five cigars, a recent innovation in the cigar industry. Only popular-priced cigars are sold in five-pack units.

Fixer

Mechanic who maintains and repairs making and packing machines.

Fixing the Color

The term commonly applied to the first stage of flue-curing, during which time the tobacco takes on its characteristic yellow or cured color.

Fixing Plant Beds

A term of local application to North Carolina and other flue-cured areas. Preparing beds for seeding and seeding the beds.

Flag

The small round bump at the end of the wrapper leaf as it is cut for the cigar. The flag is made fast, after the cigar is wrapped, with a paste of gum tragacanth or similar material, so that the wrapper is firmly held in place.

Flake

Smoking tobacco cut into small oval or irregular pieces. Flake cut is usually fast-smoking.

Flare

The tuck or open end of the cigar, which is lit.

Flash

The brightness of color in flue-cured tobaccos. Especially bright leaves are "flashy."

Flat goods

The term applied to loosely compressed plugs, famous in Winston, North Carolina, and associated with its rise to importance in the tobacco trade.

Flat Plug

Chewing tobacco made from Bright Leaf tobaccos.
see NAVY PLUG

Flat Tobacco

A term used to describe tightly compressed plugs.

Flavor

The inherent flavoring qualities of the leaf are in its sugar, resin, and oils; they may vary according to the type of leaf and the process by which it was cured. The natural flavor of the leaf, however, is seldom recognizable in smoking, cigarette or chewing tobaccos, and almost never in snuff. Casings and artificial flavorings are added to give the leaf aroma. Formulas for flavorings are jealously guarded by manufacturers. When tobaccos were more often prepared by hand, recipes for flavoring were developed by individuals to suit their own taste and were as much a matter of pride as those of any modern gourmet.

For smoking tobacco, the following simple recipe was fairly popular around 1860 and may be similar to some used by manufacturers today. To prepare the solution two ounces of cinnamon and four ounces of tonka beans are ground fine and macerated in one quart of rum. Shag and Cavendish flavoring may be prepared with these ingredients:

Oil nutmeg, 2 oz.; oil clove, 1 oz.; oil geranium, 4 oz.; oil sandal, 4 oz.; oil orange, 1 oz.; tincture cascarilla, 32; tinct. valerian, 8 oz.; tinct. tolu, 8 oz.; tinct. musk, 8; tinct. orris, 8 oz.; tinct. tonquin, 24 oz.; tinct. vanilla, 8 oz.; Spirits, 16 oz.

The simplest flavoring formula for Havana cigars includes tincture cascarilla, 5 oz.; tinct. tonquin, 15 oz.; oil cognac, 1 dram; Spirits, 40 oz.

Flea Beetle

An insect which, in the adult form, eats small holes in the leaves of flue-cured tobaccos and may destroy the bud of the seedling.

Flea-Bugs

Colloquialism for flea-beetle.

Floor Stock Tax

A Federal tax proposed in 1940 to offset the difference between taxes paid on accumulated stocks and higher tax rates paid on cigarettes purchased since cigarette tax increases in 1919, 1940 or 1942.

Floorman

A warehouse man, the bidding-starter, for instance.

Florida Bright

Common name for one of the flue-cured tobaccos produced principally in the southern section of Georgia and to some extent in Florida, Alabama and Mississippi. Government classified as Type 14 of Class 1.

Flue-cured tobacco

Tobacco cured in barns formerly heated by means of flues circulating the heat and carrying the smoke away. Flue-cured types, frequently spoken of as Bright Tobacco, are extensively grown in Virginia, northern and eastern North Carolina, eastern South Carolina, southeastern Georgia, and northern Florida. Flue-cured leaf is used in the manufacture of cigarettes and smoking and chewing tobaccos and for export. The bright yellow color of the leaf is due mainly to the character of the soil on which it is grown and the method of curing. Typical soils are light sands, coarse sandy loams, sandy loams, and fine sandy loams with yellow or red sandy subsoils.

Flue-cured tobaccos are of four types: type 11, Old Belt; 12, Eastern North Carolina; 13, South Carolina; 14, Georgia and Florida grown leaf. It is graded as wrappers, leaf and smoking leaf, cutters, lugs and primings, nondescript and scrap. Flue-cured tobaccos are used principally in the manufacture of cigarettes, though a small percentage may be introduced into smoking tobaccos.

Flue-cured Tobacco

This type of tobacco which is also known as "Bright Tobacco" is produced mainly in Georgia, North Carolina, South Carolina, and Virginia. Most of it is used in the manufacture of cigarettes, although it is also used for making smoking tobacco. It dominated both the domestic and export market by the mid-1930's. It is graded as *Class One* by the Department of Agriculture of the United States Government.

Flue Curing

In this method, the tobacco leaves are dried from heat radiating from pipes or flues. These flues are connected with a furnace.

Flyings

In Burley tobacco, the lowest leaves on the plant. Chiefly used for smoking tobacco. By government definition, a group of Burley which is relatively non-elastic, thin in body, low in oil, and which has an open porous weave and pale dusky color. Locally also called Spods.

Foom

The mouth-piece of the superior type of Egyptian pipe, consisting of two or more pieces of amber joined by gold or other precious substances.

Force-sweating

Fermentation of cured leaves by artificially controlled atmospheric conditions. The process is applied to cigar tobaccos.

Foreign Matter

Any substance or material extraneous to tobacco leaves, such as dirt, sand, stalks, suckers, straw and string.

Form

By government classification, the stage of preparation of tobacco, such as Unstemmed or Stemmed.

Fortieth

Fifty cigars.

see TWENTIETH

Forty-three's and Forty-two's

The longer length of Number Two Seconds of Connecticut Broadleaf tobacco. This grade of leaf, which belongs to the thin binder grades, is generally subdivided by the farmers into 43's and 42's, referring to government sizes introduced into Broadleaf in 1923. Broadleaf tobaccos have been reclassified, but these size numbers are still current among growers in the Connecticut Valley.

Four Hundred

A flue-cured tobacco, probably a natural hybrid. The plant is of medium height, the leaves thin, broad and medium wide spaced, usually of a yellowish cast, and contain a large percentage of cigarette tobacco. When cured the leaves are lemon color.

Four Hundred One

A selection of Four Hundred and Cash. The plant is taller than Four Hundred, the leaves have more body but are less pronouncedly yellowish in cast. When cured, the leaves are frequently cherry red in color.

Four Hundred Two

A hybrid selection of Four Hundred and Jamaica. Similar to Four Hundred in its physical characteristics. Also does well in a wide variety of soil types and conditions.

Foxing

A term used to describe a plant where the upper leaves stand upright, close to the stem. No cause is known for this undesirable condition.

France

Andre Thevet, a Protestant missionary to Brazil, claimed the distinction of having first introduced tobacco to France. But he could hardly have been as instrumental in encouraging its use as Jean Nicot, Ambassador to Portugal in 1559 (*see* TOBACCO). Nicot became interested in the herb and even planted it in the garden at the Embassy. Half-believing the claims made for its great healing powers, he sent samplings of the wonder-herb to several persons of importance in France —among them, the Queen Mother, Catherine de Medici, after whom the herb was called *Herbe de la Reine;* and to the Grand Prior, after whom it was called *L'herbe du Grand Prieur.* Later, however, it was more properly named after Nicot himself *Nicotiana.*

Fashion for awhile encouraged smoking of the wonder-herb until fashion changed, during the reign of Louis XIII, and snuff became popular. Opposition to smoking took the practical form of heavy duties imposed first by Cardinal Richelieu and later by Louis XIV, who made tobacco a royal monopoly. Both duties and protected rights, sold under the royal patent to interested contractors, proved a considerable source of revenue. As in other countries, the use of tobacco quickly spread throughout the country. France was already acquainted with the cigar by the time it became popular elsewhere, and quickly accepted the cigarette, which was favoured by Louis Napoleon, when he became Emperor in 1852.

Frenching

A disease frequently confused with mosaic, but which is not infectious and is due to more unfavorable condition of

the soil. In severe cases the leaves of the plant are so long
and narrow that they may be spoken of as stringy or ribbon-
like, and they are extremely thick and brittle. In milder
forms of the malady the leaves are small, narrow, stiff, and
stand up in an erect manner. The upper surface of the young
leaves shows numerous golden-yellow spots, and the leaves
are thick.

The term is incorrectly applied to mosaic.

Frenchino

Local Connecticut Valley term for calico or mosaic.

Frenchman

A slang expression of the flue-cured districts for a plant
with a small stalk and leaves of poor quality.

Frog Eye

A disease attacking maturing leaves causing a small lesion
(less than a quarter inch in diameter). The spots have gray
or white centers with narrow yellow, brown, or black borders.
The disease is prevalent in flue-cured and Burley areas, but
usually causes comparatively little damage.

Frontmark

The name of the size or shape of the cigar, which usually
appears on the front of the cigar box. Hence "front mark" is
used synonymously with size (shape). The following sizes
are given in this dictionary: corona, blunt, thin, cigarillo and
perfecto. These may be used as part of a frontmark or another
term of the manufacturer's choice may be substituted.

Fudgeon

The term applied to the chewing of tobacco during the
Colonial period, especially in the Connecticut Valley.

Fusarium Wilt

A stalk disease indicated by slow yellowing or drying up
of the leaves on one side of the plant and a darkening of the
inner bark of the stalk. The disease occurs in Georgia, North
and South Carolina, Maryland, Tennessee, and Kentucky.

G

Gas Bomb

A cigar (slang).

Gasper

A cigarette (British slang).

Gaston, Lucy Page (1860-1924)

Originally affiliated with Woman's Christian Temperance Union, she joined the anti-tobacco crusade in Chicago in the 1880's and became one of its leaders. She employed such techniques as pins for children, sermons, parades, and actually succeeded in having statutes passed prohibiting the sale of tobacco to minors. In the 1920's she expressed a desire to become President of the United States on an anti-tobacco ticket.

Gavilla

A hand of Cuban leaf.

Gebhardt

Common name for a cigar-filler tobacco produced principally in the Miami Valley section of Ohio and Indiana. Government classification Class 4, Type 42.

General Dawes

A style of pipe in which the straight shank is attached at the top of the bowl instead of the bottom. The smoke is carried into the stem through the space between an inner bowl and the outer bowl. The bowl is "pot-shaped"—straight-sided and flat-bottomed.

Genuine Havana

see HAVANA

Georgia and Florida Shade-grown

see SHADE OF GEORGIA AND FLORIDA

Georgia and Florida Sun-grown

A cigar-leaf of the filler type also known as the Georgia and Florida Filler. Produced principally in southwestern

Georgia and central northern Florida. Government classification, Type 45.

Georgia Flue-cured

Common name for one of the flue-cured tobaccos produced principally in the southern section of Georgia and to some extent in Florida, Alabama and Mississippi. Government classified as Type 14 of Class 1.

Germination

The viability of seed is usually determined by test before seeding. In some tobacco areas seed is first germinated in glass jars. When the seed is sprouted, humus and then sand are added until the small amount of seed needed has been sufficiently mixed with spreading materials to facilitate good general coverage of the seedbed.

Ginseng

The root of ginseng, a native North American plant growing in Quebec, Ontario and Georgia, is used as a substitute for glycerine as a hydroscopic agent.

Ginter, Lewis

One of the pioneers in the field of cigarette manufacturing. A native of New York City, he established himself as the first cigarette manufacturer of Richmond, Va. He was noted for his fine salesmanship, and his product was well packaged. At the Philadelphia Centennial Celebration of 1876, his displays won honors, and this did much toward developing the cigarette industry.

Goat hair

Fine cut filler. Also called nigger hair.

Gold Dollar

A variety of flue-cured tobacco of the medium to narrow leaf group, which is inclined to be rather oily and stretchy for top cigarette quality leaf.

Golden Harvest

A hybrid selection of flue-cured Four Hundred and Gold Dollar tobaccos. The plant grows to medium height with broad, closely spaced leaves on a large stalk. The leaves have a yellowish cast and cure to a bright lemon color.

Golden Wilt

A fairly recent hybrid of the flue-cured leaf which combines a wilt resistant strain and Virginia Bright Leaf.

Gonger

Underworld slang for an opium pipe. An opium addict is said to be a gonger or to be a gong-kicker.

Gouda

When James I exiled the clay pipe makers of Bristol they settled in Gouda, the home of the pottery trade in Holland. There they taught their craft to the Dutch, who presently developed it into a fine art, and Gouda became the center for the famous Dutch clay pipe.

Gourd

In Africa the hollowed-out, capacious horns of animals, frequently serving as pipe bowls among smokers notorious for their big appetites.

Gozeh

The Persian pipe similar to the nargileh except that it has a short cane stem and no stand. It is used by men of the lowest classes.

Grade

A subdivision of a type which, by government classification, is separated according to group and quality, and according to color when it is of sufficient importance to be treated as a separate factor.

Grader

One who grades freshly cured tobacco according to quality, size and color. The grading man may also be the supervisor of a prize house.

Grades of Seconds

The third or poor grade of Maryland cigar tobacco. Government classified as X-group. Such leaf must be clean and sound and must not contain waste in excess of the tolerances specified or of undesignated nondescript tobaccos.

see SECONDS

Grading

The selection and grouping of leaf according to its quality, color, thickness, elasticity, injury, etc., are the determining factors. Government grading was provided by an act of Congress in 1916. During the 1920's the government also did a great deal to educate the farmer in the proper grading of tobacco, working mostly through the cooperatives of that time. The Tobacco Inspection Act passed in 1935, provided for the collection and publication of tobacco statistics and authorized the government to set up an inspection system in any leaf market so long as two-thirds the growers using that market desired government inspection.

Grading, U.S. Dept. of Agriculture

The Department of Agriculture of the United States Government grades tobacco by dividing it into seven classes. Classes one, two, and three, are the so-called non-cigar leaf classes, which include cigarette tobacco, smoking tobacco, chewing tobacco and snuff. These three classes are differentiated by the method used in the curing process. Thus class one includes the Flue-Cured tobacco, class two, the Fire-Cured, and class three, the Air-Cured. The next three classes, four, five and six cover the cigar-leaf groups. Class four includes the cigar-filler type, class five, the cigar binder, and class six, the cigar wrapper type. Class seven covers "Miscellaneous types."

Grand Prieur (Prior), l'herbe de

An early French term for tobacco.
see FRANCE

Granulated

This is the coarsest variety of cut smoking tobacco, composed of small roughly cut thick pieces of tobacco. Granulated tobaccos generally burn rather slowly and therefore make a cool smoke.

Granulators

Flyings of Burley tobacco.
see FLYINGS

Granville Wilt

The term by which bacterial wilt is commonly known in the flue-cured regions. The disease originally occurred in

Granville County, North Carolina, but has spread to most other flue-cured areas.

see BACTERIAL WILT

Gray Soils

Local term for Cecil sandy loams. These have a characteristically gray gravelly topsoil and a heavy red clay subsoil.

Great Plague (1664-1666)

At Eaton, as well as at other institutions, prophylactic pipes of tobacco were given to children every morning, during the Great Plague, the smoke then being considered an immunizing agent.

Green

1) By government classification, any leaf which is more than one-fifth predominantly green. (Crude leaves are one-fifth or more definitely green). Or a lot of tobacco containing 20% green leaves. (Crude lots contain 30%). Or any lot containing 20% mixed green and crude leaves.

2) In general usage, "green" indicates the condition of all tobacco in the barn or in the field; i.e., tobacco before it is cured.

Green Cigar

The cigar as it leaves the cigar-making machine. The green cigar is then sent to the humidor room for seasoning preparatory to being packed in boxes.

Green, John Ruffin

Founder of the so-called "Durham" tobacco, and creator of the famous trademark—the Durham Bull. His business which grew popular after the American Civil War, was sold to William T. Blackwell who, developed modern methods of mass production and distribution, thru the use of advertising. Green died in 1869.

Green June Beetle

An insect which in the larval stage may do considerable damage to seedlings by burrowing in the plant beds, thereby uprooting the very small plants. The grub has the diverting habit of crawling on its back.

Green River

Common name for a type of dark air-cured tobacco produced principally in the Green River Section of Kentucky, in both the Owensboro and Henderson districts. Government classified: Type 36, Class 3.

Green River tobacco is of the One-Sucker type and is commonly used in the production of chewing tobacco, though to some extent it is utilized for snuff and smoking tobaccos.

Green Scum

A plant-bed disease characterized by a moist green growth which spreads over the entire plant bed surface. The scum is made up of minute algae, is most likely found where organic materials have been used as fertilizers, but is fairly easily controlled.

Green Spot

In air-cured tobaccos numerous green-brown spots are likely to appear shortly after the tobacco has been put into the barn. It is caused by the death of the leaf tissue (from one or more organism) before the green pigments have been eliminated in the curing process.

Green Stemmery

Place where tobacco is stemmed before aging, a process first introduced about 1930.

Greenies

Cigarettes made from unaged tobacco (slang).

Greenish

By government classification, leaves of which one-fifth or more contain a decided greenish tinge or cast; or a lot of tobacco containing 30% or more greenish or green and greenish leaves combined.

Greider

A variety of Pennsylvania Seedleaf yielding a high percentage of wrappers. The plant has fairly narrow leaves and good growth habits.

Grinding

The process of mechanically stemming cigar filler leaves,

especially grades of seconds of Puerto Rican tobacco. Also called Threshing. The resulting tobacco is used for short filler.

Gross Up

Colloquial expression for running up the price on tobacco sold at auction by trick bidding, etc.

Ground Puppy

Common term for Mole Cricket in Southern coastal regions.

Group

A group of grades, or a division of type covering several closely related grades of tobacco.

Guinea tobacco

Leaves with "frogeyes." So called because the green speckles which appear on such tobacco resemble those of a guinea hen.

Gulian

Oriental variety of tobacco grown in Iran and used in cigarettes.

Gum

The waxy surface coating of cured cigar tobacco, one of the chief factors controlling the flexibility of the leaf. With sweating the gum tends to disappear and the leaf to lose its "stretch."

Gutting a pile

Pulling a pile hard; i.e., pulling hands from many parts of the pile in order to examine it.

H

Habana.
see HAVANA

Hagerstown Soils
A soil series of the Central Valley of Tennessee especially favorable to the growing of Burley tobaccos. Hagerstown soils are basically limestone with a slightly acid reaction.

Hand
A bunch of cured tobacco, consisting of five to twenty leaves which have been sorted according to quality.

Such bundles of tobacco each contain approximately twenty-five leaves tied at the butt end with a tobacco leaf.

In the Cuban cigar industry, the band is called a *Gavilla*. It is comprised of twenty-five halves of wrapper leaves.

Handing or Handing-up
Picking up harvested flue-cured leaves in groups of two to five and handing them to the person who is attaching the tobacco to sticks in "hands."

Hand-off Man
Removes from the conveyor or storage rack the lath-like sticks strung with hands of flue-cured tobacco.

Hand Plant
As the planter moves down the rows, he puts each seedling in the hole in front of the one where the dropping machine has left it. In order to do this he must begin the row with an extra plant, and this is called the hand plant.

Hanes, Pleasant Henderson
He founded the firm, P. H. Hanes & Co., which became the largest tobacco producing unit of Winston, N. C., in 1880, producing about a million pounds of "flat" tobacco. In 1900 the firm became part of the R. J. Reynolds Tobacco Company.

Hard
Plug tobacco (slang).

Hard Cure
Shed-damaged air-cured tobacco.

Hardening
Cigar wrapper and binder tobacco (Broadleaf or Seedleaf) seedlings are exposed to the sun during the day when they have developed from four to six leaves. That is, the covers under which they are grown are raised until they can be left off entirely.

Harrison Special
A flue-cured hybrid similar to the Four Hundred type of tobacco, of medium height with a fairly thin, broad leaf of good length and a slight yellowish cast. Leaves usually cure to a lemon color.

Harvesting
Harvesting of domestic tobaccos is done either by stalk-cutting (cutting the stems of the plant near the ground) or priming (picking individual leaves from the plant as they ripen).

Havana
1) Tobacco raised in Cuba. The term comes from Habana, the capital of the Republic and, when the export of leaf began, the only port. The term is given to cigars manufactured in Cuba. These have become famous for their excellent qualities. For domestic "Havana" leaves see Connecticut Valley Havana and New York State.

2) A term generally applying to cigars which contain a percentage of Havana mixed with domestic leaf, especially cigars made with a Havana wrapper. *Genuine Havanas* are cigars made entirely of highest quality Cuban leaf and are hand manufactured in Cuba. Such cigars bear the Guarantee Seal of the Cuban Government, a green band 2 and 3/16" wide.

Havana Seed
One of the principal types of cigar tobaccos raised in this country, more commonly known as Connecticut Havana but called Havana Seed especially in the northern cigar-tobacco

districts. The so-called Spanish tobaccos are of this family.
Hawkins, Sir John (1532-1595)
  Credited with the original direct importation of tobacco from America into England. During his celebrated second expedition he obtained some leaves in Florida and brought them to England in September 1565.
Hay burner
  A smoking pipe (slang).
Hay Down
  Air-cured tobacco drying too quickly in the barn (if the season is not propitious) dries out like hay but does not cure.
Head
  The mouth end of a cigar.
Head Labels
  The pictures affixed to the tops or heads of chewing tobacco boxes, first used about 1890.
Heavy-Crop
  Maryland tobacco which, by government definition, is medium thick in body as compared with the average body of the type and which does not have the characteristics of seconds or green leaves grown near the ground. Normally consists of the upper leaves of the plant, including Tips. Also referred to as semi-crop, dull-crop, dull or fillers.
Heavy Leaf Grades
  Grades of medium quality or group of dark air-cured cigar tobaccos, used generally as binders. In Maryland tobaccos of the same type, Heavy Leaf is the first or prime quality.
Heel
  The inside base of a tobacco pipe bowl. Sometimes the word is mistakenly used for Dottle.
Heifer dust
  Snuff (slang).
Heilman
  A natural variety of Pennsylvania Seedleaf which produces a high percentage of wrappers.
Henbane, Indian
  An English term for the tobacco used by the Indians sup-

posedly for remedial purposes. Its juices and smoke were said to cure such conditions as infected wounds, fevers, coughs, catarrh, toothache, etc.

Usually *nicotiana rustica,* sometimes *nicotiana tabacum,* was used for this purpose.

Henbane of Peru
see HYOSCYAMUS PERUVIANUS

Henbane, yellow
This is the so-called *nicotiana rustica* which botanists designated as *hyoscyanus luteus.* It has been also known as *English Tabaco* or *English tobacco,* and was used as a substitute, according to Harrison, for the *nicotiana tabacum* or "true tabaco," by the English in the 16th century.

see also ENGLISH TOBACCO

Henderson Dark-fired
Common name for one of the fire-cured tobaccos produced principally in the Henderson District of Kentucky. Government classified as Type 24 of Class 2.

Henderson District Air-cured
Common name for a type of air-cured tobacco produced in the Henderson district of the Green River section of Kentucky. Government classified as Type 36, Class 3.

Henderson Stemming
A type of fire-cured tobacco raised in the Webster, Hopkins, McLean, Union and Henderson Counties of Kentucky. Also known as Northern Fire-cured.

Herba legati
see HERBE DU GRAND PRIEUR

Herba Medicea
see HERBE DE LA REINE

Herba Panacea or Herba Santa
Terms applied to tobacco during the latter years of the sixteenth century in Europe when it was considered to have great medicinal value.

Herba Sancta or Herba Sacra
As terms given tobacco shortly after its introduction into

Turqee, these refer to the divine remedial powers tobacco was then thought to possess.

Herba Santa Croce

In 1585, Durante used this term to describe tobacco. His purpose was to honor Cardinal Prospero de Santa Croce, who was credited with introducing tobacco into Italy.

Herbe Angoulmoisine

Thevet, who introduced the tobacco seed into France, proposed the above term for the plant. It is named after his birthplace, Angouleme, where he first successfully cultivated tobacco.

Herbe de l'Ambassadeur

see HERBE DU GRAND PRIEUR

Herbe de la Reine

Returning to France in 1561, Jean Nicot, Lord of Villemain, presented some tobacco plants to the Queen, Catherine de Medici, and the name of the plant changed from *Herbe du Grand Prieur* to *Herbe de la Reine* or *Herbe Medicea*.

Herbe du Grand Prieur

In 1559 Jean Nicot, Lord of Villemain, purchased some tobacco seed in Lisbon while ambassador to the Portuguese Court. This he sent to the Grand Prior of France, and for a while the tobacco was known by the above name.

Herd of Camels

A package of Camel Cigarettes (slang).

Heil Wunderkraut

A German term used to describe tobacco as a healing agent when this herb was first introduced into that country.

hhagar

The bowl of an Egyptian pipe, made of baked earth colored red or brown.

Hickory-puckery

During the early seventeenth century London merchants were allowed a refund of duties for re-exported tobacco shipments. Some merchants listed light weights for imports, a practice called Hickory-puckery. The reporting of heavy hogsheads for export to the continent was called Puckery-hickory.

Hicks

A variety of flue-cured tobacco popular in several types of soil conditions. The plant has a very large stem and usually grows with a narrow and pointed leaf but is severely affected by adverse weather conditions. Cured leaves are of a bright flashy color.

High Case

Cured tobacco of the air-cured variety is ordered or moistened so that it will become pliable. When allowed to become too moist it is said to be in high case.
see CONDITION

Hill Billies

The slang phrase applied to tenant farmers who did not join the Dark Tobacco District Planters' Protective Association, *which see.*

Hills

In flue-cured areas fields are "bedded" to receive transplanted tobacco plants. The fields are then marked off in rows by hoe or slide and the field is ready.
see BEDDED

Hobo's delight

Cigar or cigarette stub (slang).

Hoeing

In flue-cured areas, working the soil between the plants in the field or seedbeds with a hand hoe or chopping out the weeds, also by hand. Also called Weeding.

Hogshead

The large cask or container in which tobacco is stored and certain forms of tobacco are sold. Prior to 1770 a hogshead averaged about six hundred pounds, but contemporary packing averages nearly twice this weight.

Hoja de Semilla

The second sucker growth on Cuban tobacco plants used chiefly by planters and their families for their own consumption, although it is legal marketable goods if processed in the usual manner.

Hollow Stalk

A stalk disease starting at a cut or broken part causing the pith first to become watery and then to dry up entirely. The leaves wilt and may drop off. Damage is rarely severe.

Holy herbe

see HERBA SANCTA

Honduran Cedar

Preferred cedar used in making cigar boxes.

Hook

Instead of using a spear to impale the stalk of Broadleaf or Havana Seed tobacco on the stick for handling in the tobacco shed, many growers prefer a series of small hooks arranged on the lath. In this case the stalk is "hooked" and the man doing the job is termed the "hooker," especially among Havana Seed growers.

Hookah

1) (From the Arabic, meaning a round box or casket, a bottle through which tobacco fumes pass). A pipe with a long flexible stem, so arranged that the smoke is cooled by passing through water. Also called—Hubble Bubble, *see* NARGILEH.

2) Tobacco to be smoked in a *hookah* pipe, made of a mixture of khambira and normal Turkish tobaccos.

Hooker

see HOOK

H. T. L.

Homogenized tobacco leaf, a process developed by General Cigar Co.

Hopkinsville Fire-cured

Common name for one of the fire-cured tobaccos produced principally in a section east of the Tennessee River, in southern Kentucky and northern Tennessee. Government classified as Type 22 of Class 2.

Hornworm

Perhaps the most destructive insect attacking tobacco in all areas. Generally referred to simply as "tobacco worms," the hornworm is found in two species—the northern hornworm and the southern or tomato worm. Hornworms are usually controlled by picking when the field is fairly small in size, or by the introduction of turkeys. Paris green or lead arsenates are also used.

Horro

see JORRO

House-burn

Decay of tobacco in the curing barns due to decomposition caused by excess humidity. Also called Pope-sweat and stout.

House-sweat

Synonym for Pole-sweat.

Housing

A term applying to the storage of any mature uncured tobacco, especially for the purpose of curing it.

Hubble-bubble

An oriental tobacco pipe in which the smoke is drawn through water. So-called from its sound when in use.

Humectant

The hydroscopic or moistening agent used in controlling the moisture content in tobacco. Glycerine and diethylene glycol, when added under given conditions, make the leaf less fragile and more pliable without great increase in moisture content.

Humidor

A place for storing cigars where the percentage of moisture is regulated. Also, a small box or case fitted for the same purpose. Or small glass or wooden container with a lid and moistening device for keeping pipe tobacco.

Hump

A Camel cigarette (slang).

Hygroscopic agent

The non-tobacco ingredients added to cigarette tobacco to preserve the moisture in tobacco. Most manufacturers use glycerin; others diethylene glycol or flavorings such as sugar-water, honey, rum, licorice, etc. Also called Humectant.

Hyoscyamus leteus

see HENBANE, YELLOW

Hyoscyamus Peruvianus

This term, which Dodoeus first used in 1574, is a popular misnomer among botanists for tobacco. It is usually meant to apply to South American tobacco, but is also used to describe tobacco generally. The plant originated in the West Indies and the Kingdom of Peru according to Dodoeus, and was used to produce a state of intoxication. It was also noted for its medicinal value.

Imported Cigar

A trade term referring only to imported, regular sized cigars made in Cuba.

Importer

In the trade (especially British), the middleman who buys cigars from the manufacturers and imports them is called the importer. Smoking leaf and chewing tobaccos are imported by the manufacturer working under terms of either the Excise or Bonded system.

Improvements

A British term for adulterants added to prized tobaccos. These were held to be illegal in exported tobacco.

In case or in order

A term referring to leaves when they are in a pliable condition.

Indian Drug

A term frequently used in the 17th and 18th centuries to describe tobacco as a medicinal herb.

Indian Hyoscyamus

see HENBANE, INDIAN

Indianisch Wundtkraut

(Indian Wonder Plant). A variation of *Heil Wunderkraut,* a German term for tobacco used as a healing agent, especially in the sixteenth century.

Indorum Sana Sancta or Nicotiana Gallorum

(Holy Healing Herb of the Indians or Nicotiana of the French). Used by some early herbalists as a term to describe tobacco but most generally used to describe the variety, *Nicotiana Tabacum.*

Injury

By government classification, hurt or impairment to the leaf from any cause except damage.

see DAMAGED

Inscriptions

The method by which Java and Sumatra tobacco is sold in the Netherlands. Sealed bids are submitted indicating the price buyers are willing to pay. Having no knowledge of the other's bid, buyers are obliged to offer as high a price as possible.

Inventory

The stock of leaf of a particular grade, type and age which the manufacturing company has on hand. Manufacturing companies maintain large inventories in order to keep the quality of their products of an even consistency and their costs as low as possible.

Island twist tobacco

see NATIVE OR ISLAND TWIST TOBACCO

Italian Cigar

A type of cigar, generally small in size, which is fermented after it is shaped and then dehumidified, producing a hard dark shape.

Domestic cigars of this type are made from fire-cured leaf.

Italy

The tobacco plant reached Italy from many sources—from Spain, Portugal, England, Germany and Austria, and the habit was spread by sailors, ambassadors and travellers alike. While smoking was mainly limited, before 1615, to the courts, the custom quickly spread. Laymen and clergy were equally affected, and in 1642 Pope Urban VIII issued a Papal Bull, *Ad futuram rei memoriam* upon the practice of taking snuff during Mass. Threats of excommunication were not sufficiently effective, however, and his successor, Innocent X, found it necessary to issue another Bull in 1650. This latter was directed specifically against the use of tobacco in St. Peter's, for the evil custom had struck at the heart of Christendom. While in 1655 permission to sell tobacco was given to certain affiliated merchants who thereby considerably increased the revenue of the Church, the majority of parishes in Italy applied the Papal Bull with varying results. Opposition to restrictions was hardly stronger than the vehemence of preachers who saw the evil practice as a Satanic attempt to league the clergy and the heathen of North America. Still, by the end of the 17th century the practice was common throughout Italy.

J

Jack

1) Four-wheel flat truck or dolly for transporting tobacco.

2) Slang expression commonly used in Western and Central Prisons to indicate the tobacco used in rolling cigarettes by hand; i.e., for "makin's." The "Jack" is put in the "Blanket."

Jaguras

The wood fiber packed around bales of Havana tobacco.

Jamestown, Va.

Located in Virginia, this was the first permanent English settlement in the New World. Here, John Rolfe—famous for his marriage to Pocahontas—introduced tobacco, the *Nicotiana Tabacum* species, and thereby insured the success of the settlement.

Japan

Japan was probably the first Eastern nation to adopt the habit of smoking tobacco. The herb was first introduced by a group of Portuguese sailors who, in 1542, had been kidnapped by Chinese pirates and subsequently driven into a Japanese port by a sudden storm. The smoking habit quickly spread, and in 1596 the Emperor himself ordered seeds planted in the Royal Gardens, though it was also by this time grown in many coastal towns. Not until 1607 were severe reactionary measures taken against the use of tobacco.

In the seventeenth century authorities viewed tobacco with suspicion since it was a foreign habit. They also disapproved of the excesses taken by the smoking-enthusiasts, who grouped themselves into smoking societies. Fires were blamed on smokers and therefore royal orders were issued against planters of tobacco and smokers.

Failing to control the use or stop the spread of tobacco, they were soon abandoned. Cultivation of the plant was allowed, and a companionable pipe became part of polite hospitality. Korea, at this time controlled by Japan, fell heir to the practice, which spread to Manchuria and thus to the greater part of North China.

In 1949 Japan raised 2.5% of the world's tobacco. Thus she produced over one hundred million pounds in that year. Most of this tobacco is used domestically.

Java wrappers

Leaves grown in Java for wrapping cigars. These are characteristically heavier and darker than Sumatra wrappers.

Jigger

A cigarette (slang).

Jobber

Cigarette manufacturers sell their output by "direct accounts" (that is, without any middleman) to jobbers or direct buyers. These include drug, grocery and tobacco store chains, department stores, and other large buyers.

Jorro

A Cuban term designating tobacco which does not burn well, or the poor combustibility of a cigar.

Jump stick

A cigarette (slang).

K

Kabakolak

A cross between the Basma and Basibali plants of Turkish tobacco. The leaf of Kabakolak is distinguishable in that it has small extensions or lobes of the leaf which cover the stem between the natural curvature of the leaf and the body of the stalk.

Kalian

A *hookah* or Persian water-pipe.

Kaloup

Leaves of Turkish tobacco taken from the middle or lower-middle part of the plant, being a less select choice than baschi-bagli and not as poor as tongas.

Kanaster

see C(A)NASTER

Kase (case)

Another term for Order.

Kavalla

see CAVALLA

Kentucky 1, 16, 41A, 56

Strains of Burley tobacco. These varieties are hybrids developed to resist black root rot, mosaic and other diseases.

Kentucky 150 and 160

Hybrid varieties of dark fire-cured tobaccos that are especially resistant to mosaic diseases.

Kentucky boat

A flatboat used for transporting tobacco on the Mississippi River in the early part of the nineteenth century. Such boats generally carried a load of forty hogsheads and a crew of five.

Kentucky-Tennessee Broadleaf

Common name for one of the fire-cured tobaccos produced principally in a section east of the Tennessee River, in southern Kentucky and northern Tennessee. Government classified as Type 22 of Class 2.

Kentucky Yellow

A popular dark-fired tobacco with especially broad leaves. This tobacco is easily cured and has medium sized fibers.

Khambira

A blend of Turkish tobacco including flavorings. In preparation, ripe, cut and seeded fruits are mixed with treacle, buried in an earthen dish and allowed to ferment from one to six months. To this preparation may be added stored tobaccos to form a mass which can be molded into small cakes and allowed to dry in the sun.

When dry these cakes are powdered, kneaded with treacle, buried again, and finally ready for use in about three months' time. Some khambira tobaccos are prepared without the addition of stored tobaccos, in which case the fermented fruit mixture is used to flavor the tobacco directly.

Kiel Cigar

A Swiss type, long and slender, uniform in shape, with a straw mouthpiece.

Kill

To dry out remaining moisture in the curing leaf by raising the temperature to one hundred and eighty or two hundred degrees. The term has also appeared as *Kiln*.

Killikinnick

A type of granulated tobacco developed by Maurice Moore in the nineteenth century. While originally the term was used to describe Moore's type only, it gradually was used to describe all kinds of granulated tobacco. Derived from Kinnikinnick, q. v.

Killing out a Barn

In flue-cured areas, drying the stems of the leaf after the leaf has been cured.

King-size

1) Eighty-five mm. cigarettes. Also called Longies. These became popular about 1939, by which time the Riggio Company of Brooklyn was producing a million cigarettes a day,

but several companies had produced long cigarettes, especially Turkish, even fifty years ago.

2) Any large-sized cigar somewhat longer than the usual.

Kinnikinnick

An Algonquin term for "that which is mixed." A blend of tobacco with other products, usually the inner bark of dogwood, sumac leaves, some pungent herbs and oil to provide a milder smoke than that produced by *Nicotiana rustica.*

Kite-foot

An early Maryland-grown bright-leaf tobacco, popular about the time of the War of 1812.

Kleyne Taback

A Dutch term used to describe tobacco.

Knock It

An expression used by the buyers when the auctioneer is losing time trying to raise the bid. In effect, "close up the bid and sell."

L

Lady Nicotine
A popular literary term for any kind of smoking tobacco. From the title of J. M. Barrie's book of essays and short stories on smoking.

Lancaster County Filler
Common name for a cigar-filler tobacco produced in Lancaster county of Pennsylvania. Government classification: Class 4, Type 41.

Lancet
English medical journal which published articles on "The Great Tobacco Question" in the years 1856-1857. About fifty physicians presented their viewpoints, both pro and con. These articles were followed carefully in both England and the United States.

Lane, Sir Ralph (c. 1530-1603)
Introduced the tobacco pipe to England when he brought a pipe to Sir Walter Raleigh in 1586. Lane was, at the time, commander of a group of Virginian Colonists.

Langkat
see DELI

Large Cigars
Normal sized cigars, about 5 to 7½, or more, inches long. These may be divided into six classes. (All prices noted are at 1942 level).

1) Scrap-filled, which sells for about 3c.

2) Domestic, machine-made Cuban Long-filled, containing a Filler of domestic and Cuban or Puerto Rican tobaccos, a domestic binder, and either a Sumatra or a Connecticut shade-grown wrapper. Sells for about 6c.

3) Havana scrap-filled, made of Havana scrap tobacco with a domestic binder and wrapper. Sells for about 6c.

4) Long-filled domestic and Cuban cigars, where the filler is Puerto Rican and domestic tobaccos with a good share of

Cuban *Remedios.* The binder is domestic and the wrapper either of Sumatra or Connecticut shadegrown leaf. Retails for 12-18c.

5) Clear Havana, a cigar made entirely of fine Havana tobaccos. Sells for 12-30c.

6) Imported Havana, cigars made exclusively from Vuelta Abajo filler and binder with a Vuelta Abajo or Partidos wrapper. Top price range.

Latakia

A small tobacco plant grown in Laodicea (or Latakia), Syria. Unlike other tobaccos, the stems and leaf-ribs are the sweetest part of the plant, which is widely used for blending smoking tobacco mixtures. Its distinctive taste and aroma are partly the result of the native method of open-fire curing.

Laying a Chakka

The method of harvesting tobacco in the Punjab. The tobacco plants are allowed to dry on the stalk for several days or until they have turned a yellow brown. When "cured" by the sun, the plants are taken up and buried in small bundles in a pit dug in the ground, where they remain about a week. There the leaves ferment. When taken out, the leaves are twisted into rope.

Laying the crop by

The last plowing or harrowing after transplanting. During the first five or six weeks after transplanting the tobacco is plowed three to five times. By the time for "laying the crop by" the plant is usually about knee high.

Leading

Applying arsenate of lead to a growing crop in order to kill tobacco horn worms.

Leaf

From the 16th century to the 18th century, this term was used in England to describe the tobacco leaf in its natural state as distinguished from its manufactured state, or the various substitutes. In modern usage:

1) Tobacco in the forms in which it appears at the time it is stripped from the stem, or primed and cured, and the

time it enters into different manufacturing processes.

2) In the flue-cured regions, the term applies specifically to those leaves from the upper half of the plant.

3) In Burley tobaccos, a group which, by government definition, is relatively medium to heavy in body, as compared with cutters and flyings. Leaf is generally of three types—smoking, heavy-leaf, and tips.

Leaf Scrap

By government classification, unstemmed scrap, the by-product from handling unstemmed tobacco, consisting of loose, broken or tangled leaves. Leaf scrap applies only to unstemmed scrap.

Leaf spot diseases

A number of different names have been applied to the leaf spot diseases of tobacco. Among them are "blight," "fire," "brown rust," "speak," "frog-eye," and "angular leaf spot" or "black fire." There are several distinct leaf spot diseases, most of which are caused by fungi and bacteria.

Leaves

see LEAF

Lector

The reader. In a Cuban cigar factory one person every day reads to the workers, though the radio has largely replaced the lector in modern industry.

Left-handed Cigar

see RIGHT-HANDED CIGAR

Lemon Bright

A selection hybrid out of Yellow Special, which it resembles, though the plant does not grow as tall and the leaves, when cured, are a brighter color.

Lick papers

Cigarette papers (slang).

Licorice

Used even in pre-Civil War days both for flavoring chewing tobacco and "casing" or covering shipments of tobacco.

Liga

In the United States this term indicates that a certain amount of Cuban leaf has been used with domestic tobaccos.

Literally "blend," *liga* means a mixture of leaves from different fields of Cuban tobacco.

Ligero

(Light) The first or prime selection of Cuban wrapper and filler leaf grown in all five tobacco-growing regions of Cuba. Tobacco is so graded only after fermentation. It is grown during seasons of abundant rainfall and possesses little gum.

Light Air-cured of Kentucky

Common name for one of the Burley tobaccos.

Lights or Light Wrappers

Top quality Broadleaf tobacco used for cigar wrappers or binders. Light wrappers are thin, very silky, very elastic, oily, firm, strong, broad, open weave, light and uniform in color, etc. By government specifications they may be no more than 2% injured.

Line-out man

The person who seals filled hogsheads of tobacco, takes samples and tests moisture content.

Liners

Wooden hoops used to "line out" or hold in the heads (tops and bottoms) of hogsheads.

Lining up the floor

Placing the piles of tobacco in even rows before selling.

Lip-Burner

Slang expression, especially of the underworld, for a very short cigarette or a cigarette butt.

Liquid amber

A balsam or gum yielded by the sweet gum tree. An ingredient of the reed cigarette, popular in Mexico at the time of the Spanish Conquest.

List

The term commonly applied, especially in flue-cured tobacco regions, to the three or four inch ridge on which the seedlings are planted. The list is formed after the fertilizer has been spread so that the fertilizer on this ridge or list is covered by dirt.

Little Dutch

see DUTCH

Lizard Tail

A dark Virginia tobacco variety with long, medium width leaves and pointed tips. This is a heavy, good quality tobacco of the dark-fired type.

Long-cut leaf

The tobacco leaf is passed through shredding machines before it is flavored.

Long End

Portion of "rod" broken off before entering cutter. After emerging from cutter, it is a standard length cigarette.

Long Filler Machine

The machine which makes long-filler cigars. These require four operators, usually girls. The filler is automatically folded, cut and wrapped with both a binder leaf and a wrapper, the ends are also primed by the machine. The feeder puts filler into the machine, the binder layer lays the binder on an automatic cutting device, the wrapper layer puts the wrapper leaf on a similar cutter, and the examiner inspects the finished cigars for defects.

Long green

1) A variety of tobacco having unusually large, long leaves, home-grown. A twist of chewing tobacco (slang).

2) A colloquial expression of flue-cured tobacco regions for poor quality leaf, generally improperly aged, which is used for smoking before its time.

Long Nines

A type of cigar produced in quantity about the time cigar-making in this country became an industry. These were long, thin cigars, about the size of a large lead pencil. They were put up in bundles of 25, packed in barrels and sent to Boston for distribution along the coast.

see SUPERS AND SHORT SIXES

Long Red

In the flue-cured tobaccos, the small upper leaves on the plant. These are of great market value.

Long Tom

A long cigar (slang).

Longevity

see PEARL, RAYMOND

Longies

Another term for King-size cigarettes, common mostly to the trade.

Looper

The looper attaches bunches of tobacco leaves to laths or sticks so that it can be hung in the barn for flue-curing.

Looping

In flue-cured areas, attaching the leaves to sticks in preparation for curing.

Loose-leaf Auction

As the name implies, an auction of tobaccos which have not been packed in hogsheads but have been kept in leaf form. This method of auctioneering first became popular for flue-cured tobaccos after the Civil War. Today most tobaccos are auctioned off in this manner.

Loose leaves

Trash of the Broadleaf cigar tobaccos; i.e., leaf which contains over 40% injured or is dirty or inferior because of foreign matter.

Loose rib

A condition resulting from imperfect curing causing the leaf strips to fall away from the ribs. Most prevalent among air-cured types.

Lots

Piles or groups of baskets, bulks or hogsheads, or other definite units.

Lucky Strike

About 1916 the American Tobacco Company first sold this newly developed cigarette. It was the result of the innovation made by "Camels," with its specially treated Burley. Accordingly the Hills developed a Burley blend in which the Burley was cased and sweetened. George Washington Hill discovered the name for the new brand—Lucky Strikes—which was coined years before by Dr. R. A. Patterson. Then was coined the advertising slogan "Lucky Strike, It's Toasted." A specially designed package with a bull's eye circle was created, and this initiated one of the most expensive and successful sales campaigns.

Lugs

1) Any lot of tobacco, except scrap and nondescript, composed chiefly of thin and lean leaves and showing a material amount of injury of the kind characteristic of leaves grown near the ground in excess of the tolerance allowed in the particular group to which the leaf belongs.

2) The cutters of Burley plants, used principally for smoking tobacco and cigarettes.

3) In the flue-cured region, the term may refer to leaves from the bottom quarter of the plant. These are subdivided into "trash lugs," "priming lugs" or "primings," "sand lugs" and "good lugs," and may also be called "cutters." In Burley tobaccos, the leaves just over the flyings, which may include some trash.

Lumberman

A style of pipe characterized by a very long usually oval shank and short bit.

Lump

Small mass of tobacco of a given weight to be made into a plug.

Lumpmaking

Synonym for plug making; *i.e.*, taking flavored leaves, molding them into rectangular plugs of a specified size, and wrapping them in choice unflavored leaf.

Lung Cancer

see CANCER

Lung duster

A cigarette (slang).

M

Mabinga

Poor grade Cuban leaf.

Maccaboy

A snuff, usually rose-scented (from Macouba, a Martinique district).

Macedonian

Turkish tobaccos raised in Macedonia are generally called Macedonian. These include most of the flavored Turkish blends used in making cigarettes and are chiefly raised in the southeastern corner of Macedonia and the adjoining areas of Thrace. The best grades are grown near the town of Kavalla.

Machete

Cutting or shredding machine in a Cuban cigarette factory.

Madisonville Dark

Common name for one of the fire-cured tobaccos produced principally in the Henderson District of Kentucky. Government classified as Type 2 of Class 2.

Maduro

(Dark) One of the factors or classifications of Cuban wrapper and filler leaf grown in all tobacco-growing regions of Cuba except the Remedios district. The selection is done after curing.

Magnesia hunger

This disease, caused by an insufficient supply of magnesia, may appear on tobacco grown on light sandy or sandy loam soils. The green color of the leaf becomes bleached out, leaving the surface almost white. The surface may curve upward.

Main-Stream

Cigarette smoke at the mouth end of a cigarette.
see SIDE-STREAM

103

Major

The principal or leading kind of tobacco constituting the largest percentage of leaf in a lot.

Makhorka

A tobacco substitute cultivated in Russia. A mixture of stems cut fine and used as a filler by the Russian peasant in rolling his own cigarettes. The term also applies to a coarse, harsh smelling tobacco smoked by Russian soldiers.

Makin's

Slang expression specific to the underworld for the paper and loose tobacco used in rolling one's own cigarette. Also called "Rollin's."

Mammoth Gold

A hybrid selection from Gold Dollar, which it resembles, and Yellow Mammoth flue-cured tobaccos. The plant matures early, is therefore less severely affected by unfavorable weather conditions.

Mamones

The Cuban term for the suckers which grow on the tobacco plant after the topping or first stripping.

Manchado

Stained, spotted leaves of Cuban cigar tobaccos grown in the Remedios district. These leaves, heavy and of inferior quality, are used for filler in less expensive cigars.

Manila rope

A cheap Manila cigar (slang).

Manipulation

Blending tobaccos by hand.

Manojo

1) Stalk-cut cigar-filler tobacco raised in Puerto Rico.

2) Four gavillas or hands of Cuban leaf. For Cuban usage see Carrot.

Manzanita

California burl used as a briar substitute for pipes.

Marijuana (Marihuana)

A narcotic cigarette. Slang term, Reefer.

Marked Weight

The weight of tobacco after it has been packed in cases. The term has specific application to air-cured regions.

Markings

Leaf scraps and pieces of leaves dropped in the handling of tobacco. While little better than scrap, markings may be sold at a low price in the tobacco market.

Marshall, Thomas Riley (1854-1925)

Vice-President of the United States during the administration of Woodrow Wilson and a most noted cigar smoker. Once while presiding over the Senate, Marshall uttered the famous remark to one of the Secretaries, "What this country needs is a really good five-cent cigar."

Maryland Air-cured or Export

Common name for one of the air-cured tobaccos produced principally in southern Maryland. Government classified as Type 32 of Class 3.

Maryland Monmouth

A comparative new variety of Broadleaf tobacco which produces rather thin large leaves closely arranged on the stalk. Maryland Monmouth does not flower during the summer but, during clement weather, continues to form additional leaves.

Maryland tobacco

Tobacco raised in Southern Maryland, reflecting certain conditioning traits. In color and weight Maryland tobacco stands between flue-cured and Burley. It is principally used for blended cigarettes and export, is best raised on sandy loam soils.

Match Me

"Give me a light for my cigarette" (slang).

Matul (bundle)

A bundle of 420 wrapper leaves in the Cuban cigar industry or about three pounds grows weight filler leaves. In the latter case a *Matul* includes stalks cut with the leaves.

Maury soils

A soil series of the Central Valley of Tennessee especially

favorable to the growing of Burley tobaccos. Maury soils are basically limestone with a slightly acid reaction.

Mayari

The leaf raised in Santiago de Cuba in the Province of Oriente. Largely used in the manufacture of cigars and Cuban cigarettes. Yarra leaf also comes from this section.

Mayfield and Paducah Dark-fired

Common name for one of the fire-cured tobaccos produced principally in a section between the Tennessee, Ohio, and Mississippi Rivers in western Kentucky and northwestern Tennessee. Government classified as Type 23 of Class 1.

Mayo, Robert A.

Creator of "navy plug."

Meadow Nematode

A tiny worm-like creature which attacks the roots of tobacco plants. Meadow nematodes, as opposed to root knot nematodes, do not develop galls or knots.

see ROOT KNOT NEMATODES.

Mean tobacco

see COMMON TOBACCO.

Media Regalia

Cuban cigar types of medium quality.

Medicée

see HERBE DE LA REINE

Medicinal Use

see THERAPEUTIC USE

Mediums

Top-grade Broadleaf cigar tobaccos of the heavy binder grades. These are very smooth, very elastic, very oily, etc., and fairly light in color. Medium wrappers in Havana Seed tobaccos are a middle grade containing leaves of much the same quality.

Meerschaum

A fine white claylike mineral, *hydrous silicate of magnesia,* commonly called by the German word meaning "sea-foam," meerschaum is found most abundantly in Asia Minor. Soft when first mined, it becomes hard upon exposure to the air, and is carved into pipes. The best quality meerschaum is very porous and contains little sand. Some deposits have been found in Arizona, South Carolina and a few other states in this country, but it is of an inferior quality.

Meerschaum pipe

A tobacco pipe, the bowl of which is made of this mineral.

Methyl Bromide

A gas treatment for weed control in flue-cured tobacco, areas especially where black shank and nematodes are present in the plant bed soils. The gas must be held on the bed for 24 to 48 hours, and a cover is required for this purpose.

Mexican Broadleaf

A relatively new variety of cigar wrapper leaf grown in the Florida-Georgia wrapper area. Mexican Broadleaf produces a small, broad, thin leaf.

Middle Belt Flue-cured

Common name for one of the flue-cured tobaccos raised principally in the Piedmont sections of Virginia and North Carolina. Classified by government standards as Type 11 of Class 1.

Midge

An insect which, in the larva stage, damages flue-cured tobaccos by cutting the stem of the seedling below the soil surface.

Miller

Coloquialism for the moth or adult tobacco worm. This insect is sometimes the size of a hummingbird and lays its eggs on the leaves of the tobacco plants.

Mingled

A degree of uniformity. By government specification, unmingled lots contain tobacco of which 20 to 25% may deviate from the group characteristics. Also termed Mixed.

Mining a crop

A slang expression applied, during the nineteenth century, to the habit of using the same plot of land until it was exhausted.

Missouri Meerschaum

A corncob pipe (slang).

Mixed

By government definition the term is applied both to color and to group. Tobacco of the same group containing 30% or more of a distinctly different color or 30% of leaf from a closely related group, tobacco of two or more distinctly different groups, or any lot containing tobacco which is not distinctly different in color, quality or body.

Moist Snuff

Scented snuff of the Rappee type.

see WET SNUFF

Mole Cricket

A burrowing insect which feeds primarily on the roots and lower portions of the tobacco plant in the Coastal Plain region, from Virginia to Florida. Control is chiefly effected through the poison *sodium fluosilicate*.

Moore, Maurice

Developer of one of the so-called "Lynchburg pipe mixtures" known as, killikinnick, which is a type of granulated tobacco.

Moose

A style of pipe characterized by a short thick stem and heavy shank. The bowl is round, curving in slightly at the top.

Mosaic

A virus, one of the most widespread maladies of the tobacco plant. Also known as calico, walloon and, mistakenly, as Frenching. Chief symptom is a mottling of the leaves, parts of which are of a lighter green color than the rest of the leaf. The disease is highly infectious and may be carried by workers or communicated from one plant to another by direct contact.

Mound pipes

The pipes of the North American mound builders of the Mississippi Valley. Anthropologists have discovered such pipes in burial mounds in excellent condition, some of exceeding hardness and the quality of porcelain, about five inches in length at the base. Other mound pipes were carved in the shape of animal or human heads.

Mouthpiece

see BIT

Mulling Room

Shadegrown tobaccos taken from the curing sheds are bulked for fermentation. After dampening and sorting they are packed into wooden boxes for storage. This is done in the mulling room. After being packed for storage and its final fermentation in the mulling room the tobacco is pressed into bales and is ready for sale. The mulling room is also the place in which the tobacco undergoes its second and final fermentation.

Mundungus

Tobacco which is malodorous. Its color is usually black.

Must

Common name for black rot and mold appearing in piles of air-cured tobacco.

Musty

A cheap snuff, so-called from its musty odor, popular in England in the early 18th century.

Myers, George S.

In 1873, he came to prominence by buying the share of one Dausman of Liggett & Dausman. Thereupon the firm became known as, Liggett & Myers.

Myosmine

An alkaloid, synthetically produced, added to tobacco for aroma and taste.

N

Nail in the coffin

A cigarette (slang).

Nailrod

A variety of hard (roll or twist) tobacco which has been cut in lengths after leaving the spinning machine. It is made of dark Cavendish and favoured in Britain.

Nargileh (also Narghile)

The word originally meant coco-nut; it refers to the East Indian water pipe which was probably developed from the dakka water pipes of East Africa. In general reference, a Persian water-pipe where the vessel holding the water is made of coconut.

see HOOKAH.

National Association of Tobacco Distributors

A national organization representing wholesale cigar dealers in their dealings with the government and business.

Native or island twist tobacco

A special type of chewing tobacco popular with natives of the Southwest Pacific islands and a most important item of barter or trade with the aborigines. It is made from dark, heavy leaf tobaccos of the fire-cured or dark air-cured type. In its manufacture the leaf is twisted into tight, rope-like form and then doubled. A large number of such twists are also subject to a so-called casing or flavoring mixture.

Natural Leaf

Trade term for air-cured tobaccos, especially those used in cigars.

Navigation acts

In the seventeenth and eighteenth centuries the British Government prohibited direct trade between its colonies and any other country except the Mother country. In return the colonies were granted a monopoly of the British Market. How-

ever, the colonists—including the tobacco planters—always
felt that the English market was not large enough to meet
their demands. This led to constant friction between the
colonies and Great Britain.

Navy Plug

A cheap grade of little-sweetened Burley plug at one time
ordered in large quantities by the Navy for use aboard the
ships.

Negrohead

Twisted Cavendish, a form of sweetened cake tobacco
popular in Britain.

Nematode

A minute eel-worm which causes a knot or gall on the
roots of tobacco plants.

see ROOT KNOT NEMATODE.

Nested

Any lot of tobacco which has been so handled or packed
as to conceal damaged, injured, tangled or inferior leaves or
foreign matter is said to be nested.

Nesting

The unlawful practice of covering inferior grades of tobacco
with superior grades on sales baskets.

New Belt of Georgia and Florida

Common name for one of the flue-cured tobaccos produced
principally in the southern sections of Georgia and to some
extent in Florida, Alabama, and Mississippi. Government
classified as Type 14 of Class 1.

New Belt of North Carolina Flue-cured

Common name for one of the flue-cured tobaccos raised
principally in the coastal section of North Carolina, north of
the South River. Classified by government standards as Type
12 of Class 1.

New Belt of South Carolina

Tobacco raised in this area and so referred to is classified
as Government Type 13 of Class 1.

see SOUTH CAROLINA FLUE-CURED.

"A New Counterblast"

This is the final anti-tobacco tract written before the Civil War era. It was written by the Reverend Thomas Wentworth Higginson, an abolitionist and friend of John Brown.

Nicot, Jean (1530?-1600)

He introduced tobacco as the "wonder-drug" of his day. While he was the French Ambassador to the Portuguese Court, a kinsman of one of Nicot's staff made him aware of tobacco's medicinal properties. As a result, he sent some of the seeds of the plant to the Queen Mother of France, Catherine de Medici, in 1560. The leaves grown from these tobacco-seeds were used for a new type of therapy.

Nicotiana

After 1570 tobacco came to be known in Europe by this name in honor of its first importer, Jean Nicot, Lord of Villemain.

Nicotiana Gallorum

see INDORUM SANA SANCTA

Nicotiana Persica

Native Persian or Shiraz tobacco, which differs slightly from *Nicotiana rustica* and bears white flowers.

Nicotiana Peruviana

see HYOSCYAMUS PERUVIANUS

Nicotiana rustica

This was originally cultivated by the Indians of the Virginia area, and at first the colonists used it. But due to its poor taste it was gradually replaced by the West Indian Variety *Nicotiana Tabacum.* John Rolfe was responsible for the change.

Nicotiana rustica

Commonly called Syrian tobacco. Turkish and Latakia are also of this plant, which differs from *Nicotiana Tabacum* (Virginian tobacco) in several particulars. The stem is branched, and each offshoot bears flowers; the leaves are attached to the stem by a stalk and are ovate rather than lanceolate. The flowers are green rather than pink, and the entire plant is considerably shorter than the American variety. This variety is native of this country but grows wild in England and in some continental countries.

Nicotiana tabacum

A Variety of West Indian tobacco used in Spanish commerce. Due to John Rolfe it replaced the smaller but tougher variety used by the Indian Natives of Virginia, *Nicotiana rustica.*

Nicotiana Tabacum

Virginia tobacco, the variety which Sir Walter Raleigh took back to Europe with him. The plant grows to a height of seven feet. The leaves, sometimes two feet long, are attached directly to the stem, not to a branch, and are covered with glandular hairs which burst when touched. The flowers grow in a bunch atop the plant and are pink in color.

Nicotiane petite des Indes

see PETITE NICOTIANE

Nicotine

A poisonous alkaloid, the active principle of tobacco. It is a colorless, oily, acrid liquid.

Nicotine Peat

An insecticide insoluble in water developed as a substitute for lead arsenate and other soluble poisons. This product is a reaction product of nicotine and peat.

Nicotine Sulfate

Used in the control of insects.

Nicotine Tartrate

A drug used to counteract the effects of Strychnine poisoning or tetanus.

Nigger

Fine cut filler. Also called Goat Hair.

Niggerhead

A strong black plug tobacco (slang).

Nigger-lip

To moisten the tip of one's cigarette (slang).

Night Riders

The more active element of the Dark Tobacco District Planters' Protective Association. The Association, composed of tenant farmers of the Black Patch region, most actively resisted the monopolists and "Hill Billies" or non-member farmers during the first decade of this century. Raiding "night riders" were first called Possum Hunters. In 1906 some ten thousand members organized into a secret fraternal order under the name "The Silent Brigade" or "The Inner Circle," with many ritualistic symbols and signs. Their chief interest was presumably to whip Hill Billies and burn their crops.

Nitrogen Deficiency

A physiological disease caused by lack of nitrogen in the soil. It is indicated by a slowing down of growth and yellowing of green plants, especially of the lower leaves. Abundance of nitrogen in the soil, other conditions being favorable, produces dark green, rapid-growing plants.

Nondescript

Any tobacco which cannot be classified into groups of a particular type or of a single type; infested, dirty, adulterated or nested tobacco; wet, semicured or unsound leaf, or tobacco which contains waste to the extent of 40% or more.

Noodle-twister

A cigarmaker (trade slang).

Norfolk soils

A soil type famous for the production of good flue-cured tobacco types. Norfolk fine sandy loam has a sandy surface about six to twelve inches deep and a loose subsoil. Norfolk sandy loam is a somewhat heavier soil of the same type with more loam, especially in the topsoil.

Nornicotine

A compound similar to nicotine, also used as an insecticide. It is made by the elimination of one molecule of water from the alpha-nicotine compound.

Northern Fire-cured

Common name for one of the fire-cured tobaccos produced principally in the Henderson district of Kentucky. Government classified as Type 24 of Class 2.

Northern Shade

A domestic cigar wrapper leaf grown in the Connecticut Valley. Government classified as Type 61.

Northern Wisconsin Leaf

A cigar binder leaf raised north and west of the Wisconsin River and to some extent in Minnesota. Government classified as Type 55.

Nose

The habit of taking snuff or "snuffing" took form in the eighteenth century. Since it involved the nose, it gave this organ a greater social importance. And anyone who had a large nose was considered aesthetically attractive and was envied.

Nose warmer

A short smoking pipe (slang).

Nuleaf

The common name for a chemical preparation used in insect control, especially in the flue-cured tobacco areas.

O

"Observations upon the influence of the habitual use of tobacco upon health, morals, and property"

This is a famous anti-tobacco tract, written by Benj. Rush at about 1798. It appears in one of the sections of his: *Essays, Literary, Moral and Philosophical.*

Ochsner, Alton, Dr. (1896-)

Regional medical director of the American Cancer Society, he stated at Duke University, Oct. 23, 1945, that "there is a distinct parallelism between the incidence of cancer of the lung and the sale of cigarettes, and it is our belief that the increase is due to the increased incidence of smoking and that smoking is a factor because of the chronic irritation that it produces."

Octava

(Eighth). A classification of Cuban cigar tobacco from the Remedios district to indicate filler leaves of small size and light color used as domestic blends and export tobacco.

Odd lots

see FACTORY SECONDS.

Offals

British. The scrap and tobacco waste accumulated in the manufacturing processes, chiefly used for by-products. Snuff made from such scrap is called Offal Snuff.

Offtype

By government specification, any tobacco which is not ordinarily sold on the markets at which it is offered for inspection, smutty or smoked tobacco, tobacco showing the residue from insecticides or having a foreign odor, or tobacco showing the effect of excessive heat, smoke or fumes.

Ohio Seedleaf

A type of cigar-filler tobacco raised principally in the Miami Valley section of Ohio and Indiana. Govt. classification

116

Class 4, Type 42. Also called Ohio Broadleaf.

Ohio Zimmer
   see ZIMMER SPANISH

Oil of Mirbane
   A sweetening for chewing tobacco which contains an extract of bitter almonds.

Old Belt Flue-cured
   Common name for one of the flue-cured tobaccos raised in the Piedmont sections of Virginia and North Carolina. Classified by government standards as Type 11 of Class 1.

Old Field Schools
   Colonial planters used exhausted tobacco fields as building sites for schools. Such "Old Field Schools" were later known as little red school-houses.

Old Greek
   A term referring to Turkish pipe tobaccos of average quality raised in the regions of Thessalia, Agrinion, and Argos in Greece.

Oleoresin
   Oil plus resin. Oleoresin is an important factor in the burn and flavor of tobacco.

Olor
   The better grade of tobacco raised in the Dominican Republic. Used in the manufacture of cigars and cigarettes.

One-sucker
   Common name for a type of air-cured tobacco produced principally in northern Tennessee, south central Kentucky, and southern Indiana. Government classified as Type 35 of Class 3. Other tobaccos of this type are called Kentucky-Tennessee One-sucker, Indiana One-sucker, Dark Air-cure One-sucker, and Upper Cumberland District One-sucker. One-sucker dark air-cured type is used in the manufacture of chewing tobacco.

Oompaul
   A style of pipe with a funneling straight-sided bowl and sharply curved shank and stem. When the pipe stands upright

the bit of the pipe appears to be three times the height of the bowl.

Order

see CASE

Order House

The small nearly air-tight house in which tobacco is "ordered" or reduced to the proper pliancy by the addition of steam.

Ordering

1) The process of putting tobacco into a pliable state before stripping the cured leaves. Ordering is usually done by hanging the tobacco in a damp cellar or "ordering house."

2) The condition of leaf tobacco respecting its moisture content.

Ordering machine

Machines of various types to restore moisture that has been removed in drying tobacco.

Ordering Pit

A large cellar usually dug under the packing house in which tobacco is "ordered" or moistened by the natural dampness of the earth.

Oriente

A district of Cuba occupying certain parts of the provinces on the eastern edge of the Island. Tobacco grown in this area is used principally for cigar filler, and is generally called Mayari or Guisa after municipalities in this region. Oriente tobaccos are chiefly exported to European countries.

Oronoko

A variety of tobacco raised predominantly in the Maryland district during the Colonial period. With the possible exception of One Sucker strains the great assortment of varieties of the flue-cured, fire-cured and dark air-cured types stemmed from this variety; for instance, Pryor, Cash, Virginia Bright, Bonanza, etc.

Outdoor Tobacco

Broadleaf and Havana Seed are so referred to by cigar leaf

growers since these tobaccos are not shade-grown but mature in the open fields.

Ova

see TURKISH

Owensboro District Air-cured

Common name for a type of air-cured tobacco produced in the Owensboro District of the Green River section of Kentucky. Government classified as Type 36 of Class 3.

Oxford

Oxford 1 and 26 are hybrid varieties of flue-cured tobacco raised chiefly in North Carolina. The former is similar to Virginia Bright Leaf. Oxford 26 grows tall, has a strong root system and rounded leaves. It is highly resistant to Granville wilt. The color of the cured leaf in either is orange, though Oxford 1 may also turn lemon yellow.

Oxford-type barns

Flue-curing barns with ridge ventilators. Such barns, generally about twenty feet wide and up to sixty feet long, may also have ventilators in the foundation walls.

Ozer

An Asiatic oak (*Quercus Ilex* or *Cerris*) used for fuel in fire-curing Latakia tobacco.

P

P and P (Pick and Pass)
An expression used by the buyers when they find a mixed pile of tobacco. Such a pile is not sold until it has been regraded.

Pack House
The place were tobacco is stored after it has been cured. There it is also packed into hogsheads.

Pack of humps
A package of Camels cigarettes (slang).

Pack of scrap
A package of chewing tobacco (slang).

Package of pills or brain tablets
A package of cigarettes (slang).

Packers
Men who pack hands of tobacco into baskets after it has been graded.

Packing
1) A lot of tobacco consisting of a certain number of packages submitted for sampling or inspection containing the same grade and kind of tobacco and identified by a similar number or mark on each package.

2) Shading or sorting cigars according to color and shade so that the wrapper on each cigar in the box is of the same color.

Pad
A given number of cigar binder or wrapper leaves of the same side (right or left handed) taken from the stripping machine and folded together. Wrapper and binder leaves are sent to the cigarmaking machine in pads.

Pan
Literally, loaf of bread. The Cuban term given to the

compact mass of tobacco leaf in the cigarette factories before it is fed into the machetes or knives for cutting.

Panacea

see HERBA PANACEA

Panatella

A somewhat long straight cigar, in proportion to its diameter, and open at the tuck end. Panatella is a general size (shape) for a great variety of cigars sold under this or other frontmarks.

Pantellas

A type of thick, round cigarette made in Cuba.

Papeleta (Papelito)

The Spanish form of the cigarette commonly found in Mexico, made of crushed native tobacco rolled in paper.

Paper-collar stiff

A cigarette (slang).

Parejo

The term, meaning smooth or even, designates a type of Cuban cigar which is of uniform thickness from tip to tip.

Paris Greening

Application of Paris green to growing plants in order to kill tobacco horn worms.

Parsons' Cause

In 1755 a drought affected the tobacco areas and the Virginia Assembly passed the Option Act providing that all debts could be satisfied in currency at the rate of two pence per pound. This legislation, reenacted in 1758, became known as the "Two Penny Act." Since the drought caused a scarcity of tobacco with a resultant rise in market price, all creditors desired to be paid in tobacco. This was especially true of the clergy which contended the validity of the legislation. However, Patrick Henry defended the law—the Two Penny Act—successfully, and it was sustained.

see CLERGY

Partidos

The trade name for the leaf of the Habana section of the Province of Habana, in Cuba. Largely a wrapper type.

Though well suited for blending with domestic cigars, it's chiefly used for wrappers on better-type Cuban cigars. The Partido district includes the Province of Habana and the districts of Guanajay and Artemisa in the Province of Pinar del Rio.

Pastaals

Bundles of individual leaves of Turkish tobacco which have been dried in the sun and moistened by misty November winds. Through the winter months the farmer and his family roll the individual leaves into pastaals and pack them for shipping.

Patterson, Rufus Lenoir

Invented the first major cigar-making machine.

Pay Hauling

Paying for the carting. The price paid the farmer of the air-cured districts for tobacco, the hauling charges included.

PDB

The common name for *paradichlorobenzene*, a chemical compound which has proved efficacious in combating tobacco downy mildew.

Peace pipe

Pipe smoking among the American Indians had, in the case of the Plains Indians especially, a great significance. Pipes for ceremonial uses, for war and for peace conferences had a ceremonial function, and an accident to the pipe or mistake in the ceremony might cost the culprit his life.

Pearl, Raymond (1879-1940)

Professor of Biology at Johns Hopkins University. In 1938 he made a pioneering statistical study of the effect of smoking on longevity. His conclusion, that smoking adversely affected one's life expectancy, has not been accepted generally by the medical profession or by insurance companies.

Pectoral

A type of cigarette paper made from cloth and stained brown with licorice. Such paper is much used in Cuba.

Pee Dee 181

A flue-cured hybrid. Parentage is a black shank resistant

strain and Virginia Bright Leaf. Similar in disease resistance and characteristics to Oxford 1. The plant is of medium height and when cured the leaves are rich lemon or orange in color.

Pegging

Hand setting tobacco plants with a wooden peg.

Pennsylvania Seedleaf

Common name for a type of cigar-leaf tobacco produced principally in Lancaster and adjoining counties of Pennsylvania. Government classification, Type 41, Class 4. Other tobaccos of this type include Pennsylvania Broadleaf, Pennsylvania Filler Type and Lancaster and York County Filler Types. Pennsylvania tobacco is stalk-cut, dried and stripped, sized and tied in hands before curing.

Perebecenuc

A word first published by Fernando de Oviedo to describe an Indian plant. According to De l'Escluse, the noted French botanist of the 16th century, Oviedo said this term was used by the Indians to describe tobacco.

Perfecto

In general the term Perfecto applies to any cigar, usually "large," which tapers from the center toward each end. There are many shapes and sizes of Perfecto cigars.

Perfumes

Such perfumes and oils as anise, bergamot, *bois de rose,* cascarilla, cassia, cinnamon, cloves, gentian root, geranium, menthol, nutmeg, peppermint, rosemary, sandalwood, valerian, etc., are added for flavoring in most commercially blended pipe and chewing tobaccos.

Perilla

Literally, little pear, the Cuban term for the tip of the cigar.

Perique

The strongest tobacco, highly flavored, and grown in the Louisiana area. It probably owes its name to Pierre Chenet. In the 1820's Chenet developed a new process of curing the leaf in the pressure of its own juices. The industry centered on land known as Grande Pointe in the parish of St. James.

Persian

Tobacco raised in Iran. This is chiefly a high-grade, mild, slow-burning leaf used in blending smoking tobaccos.

Persichan

see PERSITZAN

Persitzan

A type of Turkish tobacco of the Basibali variety, grown in Macedonia. British spelling, Persichan.

Pesada

(Heavy). Heavy or gummy Cuban tobaccos, usually wrapper leaf.

Petite Nicotiane

A French term used to designate a variety of *Nicotiana Tabacum*.

Petticoating

Covering poor grade leaves in a hand of tobacco with a "petticoat" of high quality leaves.

Petum

see PETUN

Petum Angustifolium

An Indian tobacco of a variety slightly different from *Tobacco latifolium*. It was used for medicinal purposes.

Petum Femelle

Used to designate *nicotiana rustica*. Early botanists applied it to smaller varieties of *Nicotiana Tabacum*.

Petum Latifolium

A term used as a synonym for *Hyoscyamus Peruvianus* also known as Henbane of Peru.

Petun

The Indian name by which tobacco was known on the Continent before 1560.

Petun a lanque

see TABAC A LA LANGUE

Petuning

The use of extracts of fermented tobacco which are allowed to ferment for several days, and in which the butts of the hands are immersed. A Cuban practice. From Petum, *q. v.*

Philippine Tobacco

A large quantity, chiefly cigar leaf, is produced in the Philippines. In later years better grades of filler leaf have developed. These are grown mostly in the Cagayan Valley and exported for cigar production in this country.

Phosphorus Deficiency

A physiological disease caused by lack of sufficient phosphorus in the soil. Symptoms are slowness of growth and stunted appearance on all maturing dark green plants. Phosphorus deficiency is chiefly responsible for the slow growth of plants in the Kentucky Bluegrass regions.

Picadura

Literally, cut. The term itself refers to the scrap obtained from cutting tobacco in Cuban cigar and cigarette industries or, generally, to all waste tobacco products. *Picadura de despalillo* refers to stemming cut, *Picadura de recortes* to the scrap left over when the cigar wrapper is cut, etc.

Picietl (Picielt)

The Nahuatlan (Central American Indian) term for small or dwarf tobacco. Known thus on the continent prior to 1560.

Picker

The person who removes foreign matter and stems from the tobacco as it emerges from the threshing machine.

Pigtail

Another name for spun, twist, or roll tobacco. The term usually applies to a roll weighing no more than one pound and generally cut no more than a quarter of an inch in diameter. Pigtail is made of dark hard spun leaf, favored in Britain.

Pile

A basket of tobacco.

Pill

In underworld slang, a pellet of opium fashioned for the gonger or opium pipe. In prisons, a cigarette.

Pinhooker

A speculator in tobacco. An independent dealer who operates on a small investment, frequently buying inferior or poorly graded tobacco for resale on a favourable market.

Pipe

An apparatus, usually a small bowl with a hollow stem, for smoking tobacco. Pipes vary from the simple tube to such elaborate oriental smoking devices as the Hookah and Nargileh, *q.v.*

Pipe Mark

The initials of the pipe-maker or his sign were generally stamped on the bottom of clay pipes made during the seventeenth and eighteenth centuries, especially in England.

Piperina

An archaic term used to describe tobacco because of the sharpness of its smoke.

Pipe-walk

Pipe-hawkers in London, especially those selling clay pipes, each developed a regular clientele which he called a "walk."

Pitillo

A Cuban cigarette.

Plant Bed

The small area on which tobacco seed is grown. Also called Tobacco Bed. In the Bright Tobacco belts logs are first piled on top of the plant bed and burned. The old rule for determining the amount of plant bed needed was to leave one hundred square yards for every three or four acres of land to be planted. Plant beds are usually about 2 yards wide and are separated by eighteen or more inches.

Plant Cloth

The cloth which is spread over the plant bed to protect the seedlings from wind, insects, etc.

Planter

In Bright-leaf sections the term came to apply only to the plantation owner or landlord, who supplied the land, buildings, tools, half the fertilizers and the marketing costs, paid the taxes, etc.

Planting

In flue-cured areas, the term refers specifically to transplanting seedlings from the bed to field.

Plow Sole

A method of soil fumigation wherein the fumigant is sprayed in the bottom of the old furrow, just ahead of the plow, and is covered immediately by the soil turned from the new furrow.

Plug

The term is said to have originated in Kentucky or Missouri, where settlers first soaked the tobacco in wild honey and then "plugged" it tightly in holes bored in a green maple or hickory log. After the moisture was drawn out of the tobacco and the wood had split, the "plug" or sweet chew was removed. In domestic plug tobaccos two distinct types appear: The flat or thin plug, which is made from slightly sweetened Virginia sun- or flue-cured leaf, and the western or navy plug, which is made from heavily sweetened Burley.

1) In the Flue-cured regions, specifically of North Carolina, plug may refer to inferior leaves sold at auction.

2) A cake of pressed or twisted tobacco used chiefly for chewing. Occasionally shredded for pipes.

3) A cigar too tightly made to be smokable (slang).

Poison sausage

A cigarette (slang).

Pole-sweat or House-sweat

Decomposition due to the fermentation of excessive sap or moisture in tobacco which is being cured in the grower's barn. It is caused by minute organisms which attack those parts of the leaf that give it toughness, causing these to soften and decay. Pole-sweat does not occur until after the leaf tissue dies.

Pool

An organization of farmers created for the purpose of pooling and marketing their tobacco in an orderly and profitable manner.

Portugal

Probably no other country played so active a role in the distribution of the early tobacco plants and the spread of the early tobacco plants and the spread of the smoking habits. Jean Nicot learned of the plant at the Portuguese court (it was first grown at Lisbon in 1558), and sailors introduced the herb into India, Persia, and Japan. Little tobacco is raised in Portugal in modern times, however.

Possum Hunters

Early name for Night Riders.

Potash hunger

Insufficient potash in the soil usually produces character- istic symptoms in the leaf that are easily recognized by those familiar with the disease. At first sign the tips and margins of the lower leaves develop a chlorosis or yellowing of the surface that is often followed by the appearance of numerous small specks of dead tissue. The growth of the leaf is uneven, and the surface becomes rough and puckered. As the disease progresses the margins of the leaf may become torn and large splotches of dead tissue develop on the surface.

Pouch

A small bag or sack of leather, plastic, oilskin, rubber or other material for holding loose tobacco.

Prayer book

A book of cigarette papers (slang).

Premature

By government definition, flue-cured tobacco having a low degree of maturity but the appearance of being ripe.

Press

Hand, electric or hydraulic device for pressing a given weight of tobacco into containers.

Priapea

A term used to describe tobacco because of its supposed aphrodisiac properties.

Pricke

A colloquialism used to describe a roll or twist of tobacco.

Primed Havana

Leaves of Havana cigar tobacco which were picked early or "primed" as in shade-grown culture and used for wrappers. Also Connecticut Valley Havana Seed.

Primer

The farm title applied to one who harvests flue-cured ripened leaves.

Primera Maduro

Large size dark red leaves grown in the Partido district in Cuba, used chiefly for domestic cigar wrappers. *Primera Maduro de Corona* refers to leaves of similar color and size but of greater weight, which are used for the same purpose.

Primera Once

(First eleventh). A classification of shade-grown wrapper grown in the Vuelta Abajo district in Cuba, indicating perfect leaves of a large size and good body.

Primera Tercena

(First thirteenth). A classification of shade-grown tobacco grown in the Vuelta Abajo district in Cuba, indicating best quality wrapper used in making fine cigars.

Priming

In flue-cured belts, the harvest of individual leaves as they mature. Taking off the lower, worthless leaves of the tobacco plants.

Primings

By government definition, a subdivision of the lugs of flue-cured tobacco, composed of very thin or tissuey, pale, silky and premature leaves which are low in oil and have a dull or dingy finish.

Primings are taken from the lower leaves of the plant and are used chiefly for granulated smoking tobaccos.

Prince of Wales

A style of pipe with a squat bowl somewhat wider at the bottom than at the top. The shank and stem rise above the bottom level of the bowl and are gently curved in what is known as a one-eighth curve.

Prize House

A green tobacco market, or the place in which green tobacco is sold in flue-cured areas.

Prize Jacker or Jack Prizer

The warehouse employee who presses tobacco tightly into the hogshead until all of a particular lot is packed.

Prizing

When the tobacco has passed through the redrying machines, it is taken off the sticks, packed into hogsheads and "prized," or pressed, by a power press into hogsheads in which it is to be kept in the storage houses.

Proctor, Josiah K.

Inventor of the Stick Machine and Apron Machine, *q.v.*

Pryor

A dark air-cured and fire-cured type of tobacco, an early development from the Orinoco variety, grown chiefly in Kentucky and Tennessee. Several types have been developed, such as Yellow Pryor, Blue Pryor, Madole, and Yellow Mammoth.

Puckery-hickory

see Hickory-puckery

Pudding

Sixteenth and early seventeenth century term for tobacco made into a small roll (or pudding) usually by the apothecary. The gentleman of this time was sure to have his pudding or "cane."

Puerto Rican tobacco

A large proportion of the Puerto Rican leaf, the second most important crop on the island, issued in the manufacture of the domestic cigars produced in this country. The towns of Cayguas, San Lorenzo, Aibonito, Cidra, Comerio and Utuado are centers of the tobacco raising areas. The majority of the leaves are primed and strung on sticks, as is flue-cured tobacco. Forty to sixty leaves are tied into one hand after curing. The tobacco is shipped in rolls tied with burlap and weighing one hundred to a hundred and fifty pounds each. Puerto Rico tobacco is classified as Type 46 and divided into Stripper grades, filler or grinder grades, nondescript and scrap.

Pug

A style of pipe with a square shank and bowl similar to the Bulldog. It differs from the Bulldog in that its shank rises at an angle from the bottom of the pipe; the stem usually has a slight curve so that the bit is about on a level with the top of the bowl.

Pulling or pulling in

1) The term, common throughout the flue-cured region, for harvesting or for priming the tobacco plant. See Priming.

2) The process of stripping leaves from the stalk rather than a method of stalk-cutting.

3) In the dark-fired tobacco regions, the term for taking seedlings from the ground preparatory to setting them out in the field.

Pullings

Leaves of primed flue-cured tobaccos, ready to be tied to the tobacco sticks.

Pull-off

A process of packing wrapper and filler qualities of leaf (usually Pennsylvania Seedleaf) together without sorting or sizing. Also called "Stripped-together" and "crop-run."

Purbeck Clay

The clay used in making clay pipes in Britain, from the Elizabethan times to the present. Named after the town of Purbeck, in Dorsetshire, where it is mined.

Puro

A Cuban term meaning cigar.

Put Down

A colloquial expression of the flue-cured district meaning to bulk; i. e., to place the leaves in piles for later handling.

Q

Quality

This is the second factor to be considered in grading tobacco. (Type of leaf is the first). The five degrees—choice, fine, good, fair, and low—are determined by the qualities of the leaf—smoothness, oil, maturity, body, width, porosity, color shade, finish, and uniformity. By government definition, a division or Group, forming the second factor of a grade, based upon the relative degree of one or more of the elements of quality in the tobacco in the group.

Quauh i yetl

A Nahuatlan (Central American Indian) term for "large" tobacco.

Quebrado Primera

Literally, first broken, a term indicating Cuban tobacco raised in the Vuelta Abajo district. Leaf of this classification lacks elasticity and is suitable for filler in low-priced cigars or for shredding in the cigarette industry.

Queenes herbe

see HERBE DE LA REINE

Quid

A chew or bite-sized portion of plug tobacco.

Quincena

Literally, fifteenth. Filler leaf of the shade- and sun-grown tobacco from the Vuelta Abajo district in Cuba. Leaves of this classification are somewhat small for wrappers but are suitable for binder purposes. *Quincena Ligera* indicates tobacco of the same district and type but lighter in color and body and generally used for short fillers. *Quincena Pesada* indicates similar leaf, but gummy in texture, also used in short filler.

Quincena Amarillo

A classification of small-size yellow leaf grown in the Partido district in Cuba. Such leaves are used as binders. *Quincena Seco* indicates another leaf of the same type but not yellow in color. These also are used as binders.

R

Racking

The process of hanging laths on racks erected in the field; five or six plants (especially of broadleaf tobaccos) are impaled on each lath.

Rag

Cut filler used for cigarettes.

Raising on a Barn

In flue-cured areas, raising the temperature in the barn during the curing process, usually from 100-110 to 120 degrees Fahrenheit.

Raleigh, Sir Walter (1552?-1618)

Raleigh was probably the first man to have smoked tobacco in England. He acquired the habit in America. Because of his personal popularity and the pleasing effects which the smoke produced, pipe smoking became popular in the Elizabethan court.

Rappee

The standard English snuff of the eighteenth and nineteenth centuries, the term being derived from the *tabac râpé* first introduced about the time of Louis XIV. Rappee is a moist snuff.

Raw

By government specification, freshly harvested tobacco. Tobacco as it appears between harvesting and the curing process.

Rayado

A type of rice paper used in making cigarette paper. Rayado is distinguished by watermarks running lengthwise.

Readying

The process of preparing tobacco for the cigarette machines. It is necessary for "ready" tobacco to pass through at least one fall and one spring sweat before being used for manufacturing in the cigarette industry.

Receiving Weight

Getting paid for tobacco by weight as it is received and weighed at the warehouse.

Recortes

Trimmings from Cuban wrapper leaf, classified as scrap.

Red Fire

see LEAF SPOT DISEASES

Red Leaf

On the Burley tobacco plant, the leaves just above the "bright" or middle leaves. Red leaf is used in the making of plug filler.

Red Rose

A popular strain of Pennsylvania Seedleaf grown chiefly in the eastern half of the tobacco district of Pennsylvania. The plant is affected by black root rot and produces a rough leaf which has a low grading.

Red Rot

see DAMPING-OFF

Red Rust

see LEAF SPOT DISEASES

Red Tobacco

1) Air-cured leaf.
2) Flue-cured leaves having a red cast.

Redryer

Machine for drying leaf tobaccos.

Redrying

Process of drying tobacco in barns by hanging, or by re-drying machines.

Reed

A substance used for the cigarette in its early form, chiefly popular in Mexico and what is now Southwest United States. It was composed of tobacco and liquid amber.

Reefer

A marijuana cigarette (American slang).
A cigarette (British slang).

Regalia
Cuban cigar types of exceptionally fine quality; *i.e.*, luxury cigars, including Genuine Havanas made of Vuelta Abajo tobaccos.

Regie system
A system of state monopoly on tobacco characteristic of most of the Latin areas of Europe as well as of Mexico.

Rehandling Trade
The industry which processes tobacco for export to Africa and the West Indies, Central or South America. The processed leaf—usually One-Sucker or, to some extent, fire-cured types —is called by various names—Black Fat, Water Balers, etc., which see.

Rejection Man
The warehouse official who makes out rejection slips for the growers who do not want to sell their tobacco for the price offered.

Remedios
A district of Cuba including the Province of Santa Clara and part of the Province of Camaguey, producing mostly cigar filler tobacco leaf of high flavor and heavy body. This district is also known as Vuelta Arriba. Much of Cuba's export, especially of blending tobaccos, comes from this area.

Re-set
To plant or set out plants a second time.

Resin
The source of natural tobacco aroma. Resin is added, especially to pipe tobaccos, to enhance the flavour, give body to the leaf, control combustibility, etc.

see OLEORESIN.

Rested
In flue-cured districts, land which has been allowed to "rest" for several years and grow weeds or broom sedge. Such land is excellent for tobacco unless it has become infested with Granville wilt.

Resweated
By government specification, the condition of tobacco which

has passed through a second fermentation under abnormally high temperatures. Refermented tobacco with a relatively high percentage of moisture, including tobacco which has been dipped or reconditioned after its first fermentation and put through a forced sweat.

Return Merchandise

Dealers normally return cigars to the manufacturer if they do not move quickly enough, since they would become stale if kept in the showcase too long. Such cigars are reprocessed and sold as seconds. The government gives credit for the stamps on return merchandise cigars.

Returns

British tobacco of a variety usually consisting of Virginia leaf. Returns are used in making hand blended cigarettes.

Reworking

Resorting tobaccos that have been so mixed as not to lend themselves to classification, cleaning leaves or removing foreign matter, or retying or repacking tobacco for market.

Reynolds, Richard Joshua (1850-1918)

Son of a planter and manufacturer of Virginia, he formed his firm, R. J. Reynolds Tobacco Company in Winston, N. C. It eventually became the world's largest producer of flat goods. In 1900, it bought out the firm of P. H. Hanes & Co.

Rezagador

In Cuba cigar manufacturer, the man who selects stemmed wrappers according to color, size, and market value of the leaf.

Rezago

(Wrapper). The term is used in the classification of Cuban cigar leaf. Most Rezago grades are used as wrappers, but some may be used as binders. Thus, *Rezago Docena Seco* is a large-size light-red, somewhat spotted leaf of the Partido district. It is used as a wrapper for luxury type cigars.

Rezago Catorcena Rosada leaves, also light red, large, and of the same district, are used as a binder.

Rezagos de Capa is the term given to wrapper rejects. The

majority of Rezago grades come from the Partido district; some are raised in the Vuelta Abajo district.

RG

A hybrid selection of domestic Cuban shade-grown wrapper tobacco developed for its resistance to black shank and raised chiefly in the Florida-Georgia wrapper region.

Ribbons

Irregular strips of cigar tobaccos made from scrap and employed in short filler or, to a small extent, in making smoking tobacco.

Rice Paper

The usual paper used in manufacturing cigarettes is called rice paper, though it is made mostly of rags, with perhaps an addition of cordage and hemp.

see VELIN, VERGE, RAYADO, PECTORAL, AND ALGODON

Rice Seed

The term applied locally to Shadegrown tobacco seed of the Connecticut valley which is sown dry; that is, without pre-germination.

see GERMINATION

Riding the territory

Looking over the fields of tobacco during the growing season or visiting the markets.

Right-Handed Cigars

Cigars are wrapped so that the smooth side of the wrapper is out. Wrapper taken from the right side of the leaf is put on the cigar in such a way that the veins run down the cigar length with a slow turn. When the veins run to the right it is said to be a right-handed cigar; when they run to the left it is left-handed. If the cigar were improperly wrapped the veins of the leaf would wind around the cigar like a barber's pole.

Rimbinding

The common name for a curling of the leaf edge by certain diseases, especially Potassium deficiency.

Rim Fire

The condition of leaves affected by drought spot, which

produces large red-brown spots between the veins and causes the tissue at the margins of the leaf to die.

Ring Spot

A virus disease attacking tobacco plants. This disease was first prevalent in the Old Belt in 1950, attacking plants which were resistant both to Black Shank and Granville Wilt. It is recognized by concentric line patterns on the leaves. Common in all areas, but most prevalent in Virginia and North Carolina. May be carried in the seed.

Ripened on the Hill

Tobacco which is ripened in the field in which it was planted.

Ripios

Literally, trash. Cuban tobacco leaves of all grades which are badly broken and only usable for cut tobacco.

Roaster

Revolving drying machine for tobacco.

Robinson Crusoe

A cigar or cigarette stub, i.e., a castaway (slang).

Rockhound candy

Chewing tobacco. So called from its use by geologists (slang).

Rolfe, John (1585-1622)

Famous for his marriage to Pocahontas, he was responsible for introducing South American and West Indian tobacco into the English colonies. His introduction of *Nicotiana tabacum* into the Jamestown colony made possible the entire tobacco industry in this country.

Roll

A form of spun or twisted tobacco made on a small hand spinning machine to produce a thick rope of spun leaf from one to thirty pounds in weight. When completed, the roll is wrapped in heavy canvas and bound. Sold mostly in Britain, and especially popular during the seventeenth century.

Roll a Pill

In underworld parlance, to roll a cigarette. Also to fashion a small ball of opium for the ganger or opium pipe.

Roller

The man who applies the wrapper to mold or shape cigar bunches.

Rolling houses

Public warehouses for tobacco during the Colonial period. So called because hogsheads were rolled to the warehouses.

Rollin's

see MAKIN'S

Room

The compartment in which tobacco is hung between tiers in a curing barn. That is, the space between tiers, from the bottom to the top. Most barns have from four to six rooms.

Root knot nematode

Also called big root. Tobacco of the light sand soils of the south may be attacked by a minute eelworm, or nematode, that bores into the roots, causing them to develop galls or swellings.

The growth of the plant is retarded and in some cases the leaves turn yellow.

Root rot

One of the most important and widespread diseases affecting the plant. When attacked by this disease the roots tend to decay and the smaller roots show blackened portions. The disease is caused by a fungus (*Thielaviopsis basicola*) which lives in the soil from year to year.

Rope

Slang for a cheap cigar.

see MANILA ROPE

Rotation

Experience and experiment have shown that the best tobacco is raised on newly cleared land or on land which has accumulated a large amount of organic matter. Farmers are therefore encouraged to adopt some plan of rotation so that tobacco will not be grown on the same land for five or six years after the previous crop. Short rotations or replanting of tobacco every three years have proven effective in some flue-cured areas if not continued for too long a time. The planting of legumes such as cowpeas or soybeans immediately before tobacco must also be guarded against, since these crops tend to harbor black root rot and other diseases which may affect tobacco.

Round Tip

A selection of domestic Cuban wrapper leaf shade-grown in the Florida-Georgia wrapper region.

Row Method

A method of soil fumigation wherein only the row in which the tobacco is planted is fumigated rather than the whole area, as with the Chisel-Injection or Plow Sole methods.

Rueda

Cuban term for a bundle of one hundred cigars, a package which was formerly cylindrical in shape, as the name implies.

Run Red

A North Carolina colloquialism for house burn, used generally as a verb.

Running

Synonymous with sweating in the dark-fired tobacco regions.

Russia

In the early sixteenth century tobacco was introduced into Russia by Polish and German merchants. Smoking was regarded by the clergy as a sin and the Czar, who was inclined to take a dim view of sinners, imposed varying degrees of punishment ranging from slitting the lips to exile in Siberia. Nevertheless, the habit seems to have persisted. It was noted by one visitor of 1643 that Russians had long been addicted to the use of tobacco, though he confirmed the severity of the punishments imposed. Grave offenders, he pointed out, were generally flogged to death.

Eastern monarchs in general looked upon smoking with suspicion as a foreign custom. It was therefore not surprising that the Patriarch of Russia proclaimed smoking and snuffing as deadly sins, whereupon the Czar issued severe legislation against the use of tobacco. Thus a first offender received the knout, and a persistent offender received the death penalty.

Opposition to smoking was probably greatest under Alexis, the second Romanoff Czar, who forbade any and all smoking. After Alexis the cause was generally recognized as hopeless and tobacco gradually gained in respectability here as in other countries in Europe and the Near East.

Rust

A term used to describe leaf spotting from any one of several such as mosaic, wildfire, etc.

Rutin

A type of sugar derived from tobacco and used in the treatment of high blood pressure.

S

Sack of Bull

A package of Bull Durham tobacco (slang).

Sack of dust

A package of smoking tobacco (slang).

Salamanders

Small stoves which use coke as fuel employed in air-curing barns to reduce the moisture in the leaf and hasten curing.

Samsoun

A favourite Turkish pipe tobacco blend. Grown in the east-central part of Turkey and along the northern shore of the Black Sea. The leaf is lance-shaped and reddish-brown or yellow in color and of a distinctive aroma. This is the best of the *Baschi-Bagli* types.

Sand drown

see MAGNESIA HUNGER

Sand Screen

Revolving screen for removing dust from tobacco.

Santa Croce

see ERBA SANTA CROCE

Saratogas

Containers used for the storage of cut tobaccos.

Sassafras soil

Usually a sandy loam favorable to flue-cured tobaccos. Sassafras sandy loam contains a fair percentage of silt and does not warm up as quickly in the spring as do finer and sandier soils of the Norfolk type.

Sauce

A concentrated water extract of tobacco with a low nicotine content used as a base for flavoring solutions applied to certain chewing tobaccos popular in European countries.

see CASING

Sausage-tobacco
see PUDDING

Sayri
The word for tobacco used by the Kechuan Indians of Peru. It is estimated from accounts of De La Vega, that the word was in use as early as 1550.

Scaffold
A frame constructed for partial field curing of seedleaf tobaccos. These tobaccos are generally left out of doors for a week or ten days before they are taken to the curing barns.

Scalding
1) A leaf damage caused by burning from the sun, usually after a heavy rain.

2) Also a greenish-black color resulting from too quick an increase in the temperature in curing flue-cured tobaccos.

see SCORCHING

Schmalbaterich Indianisch Wundtkrant
A German term for a variety of tobacco noted for its healing properties.

Scorching
The reddish cast produced in flue-cured tobaccos by high temperatures during the curing process, specifically temperatures of 190° or 200°.

Scotch or High-dried Scotch
A pure snuff made from the central stalk of the tobacco plant, popular in the eighteenth and nineteenth centuries when more exotic flavours were not required.

Scrap
By government definition, a by-product from handling leaves in both the unstemmed and stemmed forms; that is, the leaves, floor sweepings, and all other tobacco materials except stems which accumulate in the manufacturing process.

In the cigar industry scrap is classified as Number One, Number Two, Siftings and Dust. Number One Scrap may be used for short filler, and number two for very inexpensive scrap-filled cigars. Either may be used for blending in smoking or chewing tobaccos. Siftings and Dust are used for fertilizer.

Scrap Filler

Any filler made of scrap tobaccos. Most modern scrap filled cigars are of small sizes. The term has come to indicate especially the poorer grades of scrap filler as distinguished from Short Filler.

Scrap Filler Machine

This machine makes short filler and scrap filler cigars. It automatically feeds the scrap onto the binder, rolls it in the binder, and cuts the cigar to the desired size. It is also called a Two-Girl Machine, since it requires only two girls for its operations.

Scrape Down

The process of pulling away the surface dirt on the hill, usually done with a hoe.

Scrub

A tobacco of poor quality which is known as refuse tobacco.

Searcher

The person who removes usable leaf portions from tobacco stems imperfectly stemmed by machine for use in cigarettes.

Season

That time during which there is sufficient moisture in the air to permit handling of the leaves without undue crumbling and breakage. This is a colloquial term of the flue-cured regions. The term appears to have come down from early Colonial times when it referred to a shower of May rain, after which time the seedlings were transplanted.

Seasoned Cigar

A manufactured cigar which has been properly seasoned in the humidor room. That is, a cigar which has had all excess moisture removed in the controlled temperature and humidity of the humidor room.

Seco

(Dry). The second factor or classification of Cuban wrapper and filler leaf grown in all tobacco-growing regions of Cuba except the Remedios district. The selection is done

after curing, before bunching. Seco tobaccos are generally
of clear color, low in weight, sap and gum. Partido Seco is
used for fine wrappers. Abajo Seco is used almost entirely
for filler.

Seconds

1) In flue-cured tobaccos, good leaves from the middle of
the plant. Such leaves are large, of good quality, and second
in choice to "best" leaves, also taken from the center of
the plant.

2) In Maryland tobacco, leaves grown near the ground.
Tobacco, except nondescript and scrap, composed chiefly of
comparatively thin and lean leaves and showing a material
amount of injury because the leaves were near the ground.

3) A local term applying to Broadleaf cigar tobaccos to
indicate the second grade of light or thin binders. These
are silky to fairly silky, elastic to stretchy, fairly firm, normal
strength, etc., and may have a dull finish and pale color.

Broadleaf tobaccos of the second quality are divided into
two groups. Seconds and No. 2 Seconds. Like the superior
Light wrappers, they are used as binders or cigar wrappers.

4) In Havana Seed tobaccos, also used for binders and
wrappers, the terms are employed to indicate similar grades
with distinctive qualities peculiar to Havana Seed.

5) In the cigar industry, the rejects which are not too
imperfect for smoking but which do not come up to the
standards required for the brand name for which they were
manufactured.

Seed cigar

A regular-size domestic cigar made of blended tobaccos.

Seed Leaf

Another term for Broadleaf, referring to tobacco grown in
Connecticut, Florida, Pennsylvania, Ohio and Wisconsin, originally from Havana. Used mostly for cigars.

Seesheh

A Persian water-pipe. The vessel holding the water is made
of glass, as the Arabic term signifies.

Segar (Seegar)

"Cigar." This spelling appeared in the 1810 Census.

Selecting

Sorting cigar wrappers by color so that each box of cigars will have the same color wrapper. The color of the wrapper does not, in its finer shades, affect the aroma of the cigar.

Semi-crop

see HEAVY-CROP

Semi-Vuelta

A district of Cuba including the territory between Consolacion del Sur and Candelaria (the central part of the Province of Pinar del Rio).

Send-out Man

The warehouseman who loads the duckbills with baskets. He uses a steel hook to pull the baskets on the truck.

Sentido

Cuban leaf of the Vuelta Abajo district which is partly rotten but which can be shredded into cigarette tobacco.

Separator

Machine used to remove dust from tobacco.

Set

A local term of flue-cured areas meaning to set out or transplant seedlings from the seed-beds to rows in the fields.

Setter

The person who digs the hole and puts in water before the seedling is placed in the ground. Also the machine on which two men sit and insert the plants after the setter has dug the hole.

Setting or Setting Out

The common term for transplanting the tender tobacco plants.

Setting Poles

The poles used to support the cloth covering for shade-grown tobaccos. These poles are twelve feet long, nine feet above ground, and are set at the corners of a thirty-three square foot area. Tightening wire is strung on these poles, and the cloth covering is placed over this.

Sewing

Shadegrown wrapper is attached to the lath in pairs preparatory to drying in the curing process. Twenty pairs are hung on each lath which is suspended from overhead crossbars in the shed.

Shade of Georgia and Florida

A cigar-wrapper leaf grown principally in the south-western parts of Georgia and the central part of northern Florida. Government classified as Type 62.

Shadegrown wrappers

A type of leaf used for wrapping cigars. 70% of the shadegrown wrappers are produced in Connecticut, the remainder in Florida and Georgia. These tobaccos are raised under canopies of cheesecloth to protect them from the direct rays of the sun and insure a fine, silky leaf.

Shadegrown tobacco was introduced from Sumatra toward the end of the last century. While it is similar to the leaf grown in Java and Cuba, it was considered the finest wrapper available. Sumatra leaf was first planted experimentally by the Department of Agriculture in 1899. It was found that, when properly shaded, the growing conditions of the native plant were nearly duplicated, and the success of the venture revolutionized the American cigar industry. The covering of cloth spread over the growing plants tends to keep the humidity and temperature even and to protect the delicate leaves from the direct rays of the sun. Within the cloth, however, it is still necessary to protect the plants from insects and disease, while an abrupt change in the weather, a hailstorm or unseasonable wind, will not only destroy the covering but much of the crop as well. Properly matured Shadegrown tobaccos are of uniform color and elasticity, are free from blemishes and have small straight veins. Shadegrown leaf is considered the finest domestic wrapper.

Shading

1) A lesser or greater degree of a given color.

2) Sorting cigars by color so that each box contains cigars of the same shade.

Shag

Coarse, finely shredded tobacco. Also, foreign cigarette tobacco (slang).

Shaker

One who loads loosened tobacco on conveyor belts leading to ordering or redrying machines. Also the individual who shakes out hands of tobacco to separate the leaves, or a mechanical sieve which does the same job.

Shakespeare, William (1564-1616)

In all of his works there is no mention made of pipes or smokers. Interestingly enough, both Sir Francis Bacon and Ben Jonson refer to the subject, and from this point of view, it makes it highly unlikely, as some scholars have claimed, that Shakespeare was actually one of these men.

Shank

The part of a tobacco pipe designed to connect the bowl and stem. In most pipes the bowl and shank are fashioned as one inseparable piece and constitute the pipe head. There is no shank in a clay pipe. In France the shank is known as the Tige.

Shape

For the shape of cigars, see size and frontmark.

Shaper

The mold used to shape the bunch in cigar-making.

Shed

The term is usually used in cigar or broadleaf areas to indicate the barn in which cut tobacco is hung to dry or cure.

Shed Damage

Pole sweat or shed burn. The damage to curing tobacco brought about by fermentation of leaf saps in the barn or shed. This term is more common to cigar wrapper or binder leaf areas.

Shell

The mold which presses cigars into a square shape. The shell is a wooden box with a firmly fastened lid. Wooden partitions separate the rows of cigars.

Shew, Joel, Dr. (1816-1855)

Prominent American physician and anti-tobacco crusader in the period of 1830-1860. He attributed eighty-seven ailments to tobacco, which included insanity, cancer, epilepsy, sexuality, impotency, delirium tremens, etc.

Shingling

1) After green flue-cured tobacco has been placed upon sticks it is laid in close rows on the ground. The stems only are exposed to the sun, and the tips of the leaves rest on the ground. In this manner it is protected from "coddling."

2) A method of hanging graded flue-cured tobacco before it reaches the redrying process at the factory.

Shiraz

Persian tobacco—*Nicotiana Persica.*

Short crop

A small crop.

Short Filler

A scrap-filled cigar; generally a cigar filler of good quality leaf used in cigarillos and other small sizes.

Short Grades

In air-cured tobaccos, the common term for leaf fourteen, sixteen and eighteen inches long.

Short Leaf and Tips

Dark air-cured and fire-cured tobacco of a medium low grade, government classified as the T-group. This group consists of tobacco which is too short to meet the specifications for U. S. Size 44 and stringy leaf which is too narrow to meet the grade specifications of the B and C groups.

Short Red

A colloquial expression of the flue-cured districts referring to smaller leaves than Long Red and still higher on the stalk.

Short Sixes

A shorter cigar than the Long Nines, but otherwise made in the same way and intended for the home trade.

see LONG NINES AND SUPERS

Short tips

see TIPS

Shorts

In flue-cured tobaccos, the fine particles removed from cut filler which are objectionable.

Shred or Shredded

Smoking tobacco cut into shreds or thin short ribbons. Shredded tobacco tends to make a rather hot smoke.

Shuck

A cigarette made with a corn-shuck wrapping (slang).

Sickle

A style of pipe with a funneling straight-sided bowl and a stem and shank so curved that the bit is brought well up above the level of the bowl top. This style is similar to the Woodstock, but its stem is more sharply curved, though not so much so as in the Oompaul style.

Side

A local term of flue-cured districts indicating the distinct characteristic of a leaf, its distinctive quality, color or length.

Sidedressing

see TOPDRESSING

Side-stream

Cigarette smoke at the burning end of a cigarette (Slang).
see MAIN-STREAM

Siftings

The third classification of scrap produced in the manufacture of cigars. (No. 1 Scrap, No. 2 Scrap, Siftings and Dust). Siftings include very fine particles of scrap not usable in pipe tobaccos or for scrap filler. Siftings are sold for fertilizer and chemicals.

Silent Brigade

see NIGHT RIDERS

Silk Leaf

A flue-cured variety of tobacco with a smooth, elastic and oily leaf of moderate yield and a slightly greenish cast.

Silky Pryor

A type of dark-fired tobacco especially popular on high quality chocolate soils. The leaves of this plant are relatively long and the fibers small.

Silver Dollar

A flue-cured selection grown chiefly in the Old Belt region, similar in characteristics to Gold Dollar except that the leaf is larger and wider. The cured leaf is bright and flashy but of a large percentage of lugs.

Similar

A degree of uniformity. By government specification, similar lots contain tobacco of which 15 to 20% may deviate from the group characteristics.

Sirdily

(Ox-tongue). A subdivision of the Basma plant, distinguished from other Turkish tobaccos by its long lance-like leaves which are shaped, as the name implies, like an ox-tongue.

Size

1) To grade or classify leaf by grade; that is, by its size, color, maturity, condition, etc. A colloquial expression of the flue-cured regions.

2) The length of the leaf.

3) In cigarettes, the length. Standard size cigarettes are two and three-quarters inches long and one and a sixteenth inches in circumference.

see KING-SIZE

4) In cigars, the shape of the cigar, indicated by a variety of names which have come to have but little significance. The size of the cigar is indicated on the box by the frontmark, which see. In general, the shape or size of the cigar may be indicated by the terms Corona, Blunt, Thin, Cigarillo and Perfecto, which see.

Skipper

A cigar in which there is a gap between adjoining sections of wrapper (slang).

Slaughter

A variety of Pennsylvania Seedleaf with a leaf particularly broad at the base.

Sledder

One who drives the mule pulling a cart or sled loaded with freshly pulled leaves.

Sleep

Cigarette tobacco is stored (it sleeps) in the manufacturers' barns one and a half to three or more years before it is prepared for processing. Preferably it should be at least two and a half years old before being processed.

Slow Burners

Fresh cigarettes. This is a slang word of underworld usage. Cigarettes, used as a medium of exchange in most prisons, are slow burning when fresh but may lie unused for some time and so become stale and fast-burning.

Smithfield

Making a bid by a nod but calling aloud at the same time a lower price in order to trick the other buyers. This practice is said to have originated in Smithfield, N. C.

Smoked

Common name for one of the fire-cured tobaccos raised principally in the Piedmont and mountain sections of Virginia. Government classified as Type 21 of Class 2.

Smoked sausage

A cigar (slang).

Smokers

1) A colloquial expression indicating all grades of leaf used to make cigars. These may include certain flue-cured as well as air or fire-cured tobaccos.

2) In the cigar trade, the cigars issued each day to factory workers without charge who, by government rules, are permitted three. These are usually seconds.

Smokestack

A smoking pipe (slang).

Smoking

From earliest times smoke played a part in man's worship. The idea that fire came from the sun and that smoke might therefore be purifying, together with the discovery of incense, made smoke a necessary concomitant of many early religious ceremonies. The first complete records of the use of incense come from Egypt and from contemporary practices of the Assyrians and Hebrews. Incense also appeared in early Greece, where the practice of burning offerings and fragrant spices to the gods was probably introduced in the sixth or seventh centuries B.C. Homer indicates that smoke was used as a purifying agent, and Hippocrates, father of medicine, advises its use by injection and inhalation to cure certain diseases. Pliny of the Romans suggests the use of a reed, a sort of pipe, in the latter case. But smoking as it is practiced today, was not mentioned by any classic writer.

The religious connotations of smoke were also apparent in the religious practices of South and North America, where the tobacco plant was native. Tobacco was especially valued for the narcotic sensation which it produced. It is evident that the religious practices of the Mayan peoples included not only smoke but also a pipe of an early form. Tobacco, used by descendants of these early pipes, may be presumed to have been the ingredient smoked.

Since smoke rises and appears to form clouds, certain Mexican Indians believed that Tobacco was the incarnation of the wife of Tlaloc, god of rain. Certain Brazilian Indians, the Caribs, thought that their warriors became more courageous when smoke was blown upon them. And certain Indians of Virginia would appease their angry gods by casting tobacco on stormy waters.

Among the descendants and inheritors of the Mayan civilization, the Aztecs are notable. With the Aztecs, smoking was enjoyed by priests and soldiers alike. Perhaps it is they who made smoking a pleasure as well as a ritual. Montezuma and his chieftains customarily "lit up" after a meal and the Aztecs were probably as quick as later Europeans to adopt the smoking habits of their social betters. Undoubtedly it was the Aztecs who, in conquering nearly all of Central America, spread the use of tobacco through much of South as well as Central America.

North American Indians, perhaps not so far removed in

habits and origin from their southern contemporaries, were
also known to have used tobacco for smoking, employing
crude pipes for this purpose. Such pipes, valued among the
natives' earthly possessions, have been unearthed in archaeo-
logical excavations of ancient burial mounds. The importance
of the pipe, especially as a necessary artifice of religious ceremony, has come down to more modern times where the
tribal pipes of the Plains Indians played so important a part
in the struggles of settlers. Many Indian tribes had special
pipes for peace, for war and occasions of state. The ritualistic
significance of the peace pipe is well known, for a pact signed
by the smoking of a peace pipe was not easily broken.

Aboriginal uses of tobacco are still left to conjecture. But by
1492 tobacco smoking was a well-established custom among the
Indians that met Columbus and brought him balls of cotton
and a strong-smelling herb which the natives called by a
word that sounded like "tobacco." It was not, however, on
the shores of North America that Columbus first came into
contact with the smoking habit, but in Cuba where his men,
sent ashore to search for gold, found natives inhaling the
pungent exhilarating smoke of certain dried leaves. Upon his
return the following year, Columbus commissioned Romano
Pane, one of the missionary monks who had sailed with him,
to write a book describing the customs of the natives. Pane
called the book *De insularium ritibus* (The Customs of the
Islanders, 1497) and in it he described smoking among the
natives of San Domingo, especially by the priests who thereby
convinced the uninitiated that they inhaled an inspiring pro-
phecy directly from the gods.

The term *tobacco* was not taken from Pane's book but
from the additions made on his comments by Gonzalo Fernandez de Oviedo y Valdes, a former sailor with Columbus.
Fernandez described smoking as one of the evil practices of
the natives, who called the herb "tabaco."

When Cortes, burning his ships at Tabasco, broke into
Aztec territory, natives pledged him their good will with

artistically carved pipes full of the fragrant herb and aug-
mented their smoking with snuff. Spanish and Portuguese
sailors and adventurers who followed Columbus, de Grijalva,
Cortes and Cabral, discovered the pleasure of smoking and
snuffing which the natives had found before them. Sailors
and adventurers were quick to take up the habit and pass
it to their fellows. Frequent voyages and more extensive
exploration did much to spread the use of tobacco and, from
the first, provided an opportunity for sermons, laws and profits.

   see TOBACCO

Smoking-leaf

By government specification, a subgroup of Leaf composed
of relatively thin, nonelastic, very ripe, grainy, and porous
leaves; being relatively low in oil, and characterized by a
somewhat duller finish than the corresponding colors of the
leaf group.

Smutchin

Colloquial seventeenth century Irish term for snuff.

Smyrna

A very aromatic Turkish tobacco raised along the west
coast of that country and used for blending pipe tobaccos.
The leaf falls into the *yaka kaloup* classification and is of an
inferior combustibility.

Snipe

A slang expression, especially of the underworld, for discarded cigar or cigarette butts. The person who collects such
butts may also be called a sniper.

Snipe shooting

Salvaging discarded cigarette or cigar butts (slang).

Snoose

Slang for snuff.

Snow Barn

A specially constructed barn for the curing of tobacco.
Invented by Wm. Henry Snow (1825-1902). Snow modified
the usual formula for curing and developed a method of
hanging unprimed tobacco on sticks in large "Snow barns,"
which he manufactured and sold.

Snuff

Powdered tobacco which is to be sniffed into the nostrils, held against the lip or chewed. Originally popular on the continent where it was supposed, during the late sixteenth to the early eighteenth centuries, to have great medicinal properties. Snuff was most popular between 1820 and 1830 when, especially in England, it was used by both men and women. Originally snuff was individually ground, called *tabac rapé* made from a small roll called a *carotte* (which see).

see also DRY, MACCABOY, MOIST, RAPPEE, SCOTCH AND SWEDISH.

Snuff-dipper

One who dips snuff; i.e., one who uses snuff by dipping a small wooden "brush" into snuff and spreading it on his gums.

Snuff mills (Eng.)

Originally the small wooden mill, similar to the pepper grinder, in which snuff was ground. By the nineteenth century, however, the term had come to mean any wooden container for ground snuff which resembled the original mill.

Snuff rasp

Formerly snuff was carried in plug or rope form. The desired amount was grated on a rasp carried for this purpose. Many of these were elegant contrivances up to six inches long with a lid protecting the grater and a compartment below the grater to store a quantity of tobacco.

Snuffing

Taking snuff or inhaling powdered tobacco.

Socking

Slang expression of the Colonial period referring to the stealing of tobacco from ships and wharves. In the 1630's some fifty tons were reported "socked" from London wharves in one year.

Soft-curing

A fairly recent method of fire-curing by means of wood fires which give a low temperature and a considerable amount of smoke. This method permits a more continuous firing and it is not necessary so often to put out the fires and permit the tobacco to soften before continuing the firing process. Soft-curing is entirely similar to air-curing when some heat is supplied to keep the temperature constant.

Sokia

An area in the Smyrna district (ancient Ephesus), near the Aegean Sea, which, together with the Aya-Solouk district, produces the most aromatic of Turkish tobaccos.

Soldier

A lighted or whole cigar or cigarette, as against a "Dead Soldier" or stub (slang).

Sorbitol

An alcohol belonging to the same chemical family as glycerine and used for many of the same purposes as glycerine. It is used to help control the moisture content of tobacco, cork and papers.

see HYDROSCOPIC AGENT.

Sore Shin

A common type of stem rot that occurs chiefly throughout the flue-cured areas. The stalk of the affected plant turns brown and smooth, and the pith is also brown.

Sorting

Grouping tobacco according to the length of the leaf.

Sound

Tobacco is said to be sound when it is free from damage.

South Carolina flue-cured

Common name for one of the flue-cured tobaccos produced principally in the coastal sections of South Carolina and the southeastern counties of North Carolina, south of the South River. Government classified as Type 13 of Class 1.

Same as New Belt of South Carolina, Southeastern Bright, and Southeastern Flue-cured.

Southeastern bright and Southeastern flue-cured

Government Type 13 of Class 1.

see SOUTH CAROLINA FLUE-CURED

Southern Bright

Another name for flue-cured or "Virginia" flue-cured tobaccos.

Southern Flue-cured

Common name for one of the flue-cured tobaccos produced principally in the southern sections of Georgia and to some extent in Florida, Alabama and Mississippi. Government classified as Type 14 of Class 1.

Southern Maryland

1) Common name for a type of air-cured tobacco grown principally in southern Maryland. Government classified as Type 32 of Class 3.

2) The area which, by common reference, includes the counties of Prince George, Anne Arundel, Charles, Calvert, and St. Marys.

Southern Shade

A cigar-wrapper leaf grown principally in southwestern Georgia and in the central part of northern Florida. Government classified as Type 62.

Southern Stem and Root Rot

A disease causing plant wilt and decay toward the end of the season. Small, round, amber-colored bodies adhering to the decayed stem surface identify this disease. Common throughout eastern Virginia, eastern North Carolina, South Carolina, and Georgia.

Southern Wisconsin Cigar Leaf

A binder leaf raised south and east of the Wisconsin River, extending into Illinois. Government classified as Type 54.

Spades

Colloquial expression for all lower but marketable leaves on the flue-cured tobacco plant.

Spanish Cedar

Cedar wood, grown in Cuba, most favoured for making cigar boxes. This wood is famous for its qualities which tend to improve the taste, even of the finest cigars.

Spanish Varieties

Certain varieties of cigar leaf are called Spanish, as Comstock Spanish, Zimmer Spanish, etc. The term was originally used to distinguish West Indian cigar tobacco from Virginia or Maryland leaf, but since has lost its original significance.

Spear or Spearhead

"Outdoor" or Broadleaf and Havana Seed tobaccos are cut so that the stalk may be impaled on the stick which is hung in the curing shed. At the end of the stick is a sharp metal spear or spearhead which is driven through the stalk. The person performing this operation is called the "spearer." Hooks are preferred by some growers, especially of Havana Seed.

Speck

see LEAF SPOT DISEASES

Spinner

The operator of a spinning machine; i.e., the person who feeds tobacco leaves into a machine which twists or rolls them into a long coil. This machine is used in making roll, twist, pigtail, and nailrod.

Spinning Machine

The machine, usually of fairly simple construction, which rolls or twists tobacco leaves that are fed to it by the spinner. Such leaves are generally coated with olive oil, and the final product of hard tobacco is almost always black. *see* ROLL.

Spit

The body or consistency of a leaf.

Spit and a drag

A chew and a smoke (slang).

Spit-and-run

Chewing tobacco (slang).

Spitting basins

It was usual for gentlemen smokers of Restoration London to sport a silver basin to spit in. The more scientific-minded went so far as to measure the amount of saliva expectorated each day to determine the effect of the tobacco on the system.

Splitting the middle

see BUSTING THE MIDDLE

Spods

see FLYINGS

THE SPITTING BASIN

Snuff-taking was a necessary accomplishment for the well-turned-
out Cavalier of Charles II's time.
The Stuart gallant's parapher-
nalia sometimes included a spitting basin, here reproduced from
the cover of a period snuff box.
By measuring the amount of daily
expectoration the scientific-minded Cavalier might hope to determine the effect of tobacco upon
his system as well as the amount
of snuff taken.

—*Arents Tobacco Collection, New York Public Library.*

DOUBLE INSTRUMENT FOR INHALING

By means of this double instrument these West Indian friends are blowing narcotic powders into each other's nostrils. According to Crevaux, one of the first writers to comment on the smoking habits of early West Indian tribes, such a device was popular among certain of these tribes.

—*Arents Tobacco Collection, New York Public Library.*

Sponge-rock
A type of stone which when pulverized is suitable as a tobacco humidifying agent.

Sponging
Splotches of red and brown appearing on the surface of the leaf of flue-cured tobacco when the leaf contains too much moisture during the early stages of curing.

Spoonbill
A small hand-truck.

see DUCKBILL

Spreading
Spreading cigar filler leaf on screens for drying before it is sent to the machine which incorporates it in a cigar.

Springfield fire-cured
Common name for one of the fire-cured tobaccos produced principally in a section east of the Tennessee River, in southern Kentucky and northern Tennessee. Government classified as Type 22 of Class 2.

Sprouting
Soaking the seed before planting so that it will sprout. The term also applies to the act of applying (sowing) the seed in a water solution.

Square Coop
A means of packing flue-cured tobacco in the packing house so that all the leaves are inward, the butt of the leaves showing on the outside.

Squaring
The stage at which seedlings begin to take on a full-leafed solid appearance, usually two and a half or three months after the seed is planted.

Stalk-cut
Cigar tobaccos raised in Pennsylvania and Connecticut (with the exception of Connecticut Shadegrown varieties) are cut from the plant with the leaf-stalk still attached to the leaf. They are hung in the curing sheds (or tobacco sheds) by the stalk.

For Stalk-cut Havana, *see* CONNECTICUT VALLEY HAVANA SEED

Stalk Position

The position of the leaf on the stalk, one of the factors considered in predicting tobacco grades.

Starter

The man employed by the warehouse to appraise the tobacco and make the first bid.

State

Tobacco sold to convicts (slang).

Steamdrying

The customary method for preparing unfermented tobacco for storage, by means of a redrying machine or steam-conditioning equipment.

Steaming

A method of sterilizing permanent plant beds by means of turning steam into a large inverted "pan" so that the ground is thoroughly saturated before the pan is moved.

Stem

1) The part of a tobacco pipe from the bowl outwards in a clay, or connecting the shank with the bit in a briar. Sometimes erroneously called the Mouthpiece. It is more or less synonymous with Bit. In France it is known as the Tuyaut.

2) To remove the stem and midriff from tobacco leaves.

Stem-drying stage

This is the last stage in curing flue-cured tobacco.

Stem-flattening

A process of crushing moistened stems after they have been removed from the leaves so that in their flattened condition a certain percentage can be added to cut tobacco without detection.

Stemming

1) Removing most of the stem from the leaves, either by hand or by a machine. In Havana tobaccos only the portion of the stem which extends beyond the base of the leaf is removed, since the stem of Havana does not affect the taste as in other tobaccos.

2) The term has a local application referring to a specific low grade of Broadleaf and Havana Seed cigar tobaccos. Such leaves cannot be classified along any of the seven basic qualities or grades of the Broadleaf tobaccos and yet do not contain trash, which may be over 40% injured.

Stemming District Dark

Common name for one of the fire-cured tobaccos produced principally in the Henderson District of Kentucky. Government classified as Type 24 of Class 2.

Stems

The tobacco by-product which is composed of the midribs of tobacco leaves.

Sterility

The medical advisors to certain Eastern monarchs once thought that tobacco caused sterility, since it was regarded as "hot and dry," the two "humours" most commonly associated, in the seventeenth century, with this condition.

Sterilizing

Tobacco beds of the cigar tobacco types are usually sterilized before the seed is sown. This is to insure freedom from infectious disease, to kill weeds and to put heat into the ground. It is accomplished by forcing steam under a low metal cover which fits tight on the ground.

Stick Machine

A redrying machine wherein closely packed sticks of tobacco are placed and hot air is circulated. Originally invented by Josiah K. Proctor in 1895.

Stick Racks

Wooden racks on which the packers put the sticks employed to hold a number of hands of tobacco together.

Stiff market

Strong market with active bidding.

Stinker

A cheap cigar or cigarette (slang).

Stogie

A general term in vernacular for any cigar, especially an inexpensive brand. The stogie originated as the long thin handrolled cigar which drivers of Conestoga wagons produced for their own consumption. When they had a surplus supply or could use these cigars for barter they left a number with the merchant of the general store to be sold at his discretion. The stogie was frequently a hard and not unusually an inferior piece of goods, so that the term came to be applied to a handmade cigar of uncertain shape and size.

Stoop tobacco

A cigar or cigarette stub salvaged from the street (slang).

Stopper

The utensil with which tobacco was pressed into the pipe. During the sixteenth and seventeenth centuries tobacco stoppers took on elaborate and fanciful forms.

Storm Tobacco

Tobacco which has been cut by hail or damaged by wind.

Stouts

A term used to designate tobacco of the heavy leaf grades of dark air-cured (cigar) tobaccos. *See* Heavy Leaf Grades.

Stramonium cigarettes

Cigarettes made in the State tobacco factory at Athens, Georgia, for asthma sufferers.

Streak

1) A virus disease attacking tobacco plants, generally individually, but the attack is sudden and the symptoms are severe. Plants attacked develop puckering and curling of the young leaves, the stalk shows depressed dead areas, and the midribs become streaked. The plant may recover, except in affected parts. The disease is fairly common in Burley areas and in Wisconsin.

2) Streak is occasionally used, especially in the flue-cured districts, as a slang expression to indicate the bruise or mark of mishandling on the leaf.

String Method

A method of laying out rows of flue-cured tobacco so that each row has a slight but continuous grade and soil loss is kept at a minimum.

Stringing

In flue-cured areas, attaching the leaves to sticks in preparation for curing. The string is attached to one end of the stick and near this end it is passed once around the stems of three to five leaves, then is drawn diagonally to the opposite side of the stick and similarly looped around a second bunch of leaves, etc.

Strip Feeder

The person who feeds tobacco into drying machines and spreads it evenly on conveyor belts.

Stripped Straight

Air-cured tobacco which are unsorted. Same as Pull-off.

Stripped-together

see PULL-OFF

Stripping

1) In "outdoor" or Havana Seed and Broadleaf tobaccos, the stalk is cut with the leaf and not separated from the leaf until after the curing process. Removal of the leaf from the stalk is called stripping and is done before the leaf is sold.

2) In the cigar industry generally, removing the two whole sides of a leaf from the stem. This is usually done by a machine which cuts the stem from the middle of a handspread leaf.

3) The two whole sides of a leaf from which the stem has been removed. Also a lot composed of such strips.

Strut or Strutting

In air-curing barns the spoilage which occurs from excess moisture. *See* HOUSE-BURN and POLE-SWEAT.

Stub

1) the discarded end of a burned cigarette or cigar.

2) the mouthpiece end of a cigarette.

Stud

A style of straight-stemmed pipe with a round flat-bottomed "pot" bowl.

Stummel

The bowl and shank of a briar or wooden pipe. In France, the Ebauchon.

Stumpen cigar
A short cigar open at both ends. (Colloquial.)

Subgrade
By government definition, any grade modified by a special factor or subgroup symbol.

Subgroup
In government grading, a group formed by the substitution of a different group symbol to denote a modification of the specifications or to indicate a certain side or characteristic of the tobacco.

Substitutes
In British manufacturing, all leaves other than those grown in the United States are known as substitutes. These include Turkish, continental and Oriental tobaccos.

Suckering
Removing suckers so that the tobacco will develop weight.

Suckers
Second growths of leaves on plants from which the first leaves of commerical value have been stripped. See Breaking Suckers.

Sumatra Tobacco
Leaves of tobacco raised in Sumatra for wrapping cigars. These leaves make notably fine, elastic wrappers.

Sumatra tobacco was imported to this country and first raised experimentally in 1899. It is now produced domestically as Shadegrown tobacco and raised in the Connecticut Valley as a cigar wrapper leaf.

Sumatra wrappers
The import into the United States of wrapper leaf raised in Sumatra became an important factor about 1883, at which time a special duty was placed on the leaf to protect the domestic industry. From that time until about 1910 cigar manufacturers in this country were importing about four and a half million pounds a year. Seed of the type later called Shadegrown Connecticut cigar wrapper leaf was brought over from Sumatra about 1899 and first successfully raised in this

country in 1900. It came rapidly to replace Sumatra tobaccos; since the last war very little leaf has been imported from Sumatra. Local term for Sumatra tobacco is Deli.

Sunburn

Cut plants which have been laid on the ground under a too-hot sun will develop sunburn. Small green spots will appear which, because of the chemical change in the leaf, will be bitter to the taste.

Sun-cured

Tobacco that has been cured by exposure to the sun.

Supers

The domestic name for a type of cigar first produced when cigar-making in this country was becoming an industry—about 1810. These were popular rolled cigars with a twist that would kink the wrapper at the end to prevent its unrolling.

Sweating

The process of fermenting tobacco. This may be done by natural means; *i.e.*, by allowing packed tobacco to ferment under controlled conditions. It may also be done by artificial means; *i.e.*, increasing the temperature and humidity in storage rooms in order to shorten the length of time required to ferment the tobacco.

Swedish snuff

Very coarse, highly flavored very moist snuff. So-called because it is used extensively by the Swedes. In Sweden the per capita consumption of snuff is eight or ten times as great as in this country. Also sold as or referred to as Copenhagen.

Sweet-S(c)ented

A variety of *Nicotiana Tabacum* which was considered by many as the best tobacco of colonial Virginia.

Sweet Soil

A term of restricted usage usually indicating soil which reacts quickly to any chemical change; *i.e.*, soil highly charged with necessary chemical ingredients.

Sweetening

Casing solution or sauce used on tobacco. *See* SAUCE.

Swirr-Hibshman

A popular variety of Pennsylvania Seedleaf characterized by rather wide leaves, narrow at the heel and medium spaced on the stalk. The plant has a high resistance to black root rot, which its forerunner, Swarr, has not.

Switzerland

While tobacco was regarded early in Switzerland, as a useful herb in the curing of certain physical ills, references indicate that as early as 1616 tobacco was used for smoking and snuffing. Pedlars and "tobacco makers" appeared from Germany and by 1645 various prohibitions had been issued against them in most Swiss towns. In 1652 the first general edict made smoking a legal offence, with a fine of two florins.

Under Calvin's influence, in independent Switzerland (newly independent after the Peace of Westphalia) an increasing number of sins were listed and deplored. Among them was "tobacco drinking." Punishments were instituted, but the habit continued to grow and the laws kept pace with the popularity of the offence. In 1670 the Swiss National Assembly was forced to admit that the severest edicts it had ordered were being ignored and that there was a growing spirit of rebellion among the people in regard to the use of tobacco. The city of Basle, center of the tobacco trade, put up an especially strong resistance. Men, women and servants, young and old, had taken up the habit of smoking. Despite the actions of a special "Tobacco Chamber" of the High Court of Inquiry at Berne, nothing seemed effectively to impede the progress of tobacco smoking throughout the country and beyond, into Austria.

Syria

The source of Latakia, chiefly at Laodice, Kavalla and Kanthi.

T

Tabac a la langue
This term is derived from the tobacco-leaf which is shaped like the tongue of an ox.

Tabac des Amazones
A tobacco noted for its sweet scent and grown in the Antilles Islands.

Tabac en Andouille
Tobacco in the form of twists. It was often exported from colonial America in this form.

Tabac rape
Twist or cane tobacco, grated or rasped as required by 18th century snuffers. *see* RAPPEE.

Tabacco Anglicum
see ENGLISH TOBACCO

Tabaco
The earliest common form of the word tobacco.

Tabaco de Sacerdotes
(Priests' Tobacco). European name for high grade tobacco.

Tabagies
Early meeting places in sixteenth century England where pipes and tobacco were to be sold. Tabagies served as local meetinghouses and men's clubs. By the end of Elizabeth's reign pipes could be rented in the taverns, thus obviating the Tabagies, where liquor was not served.

Tabaquito
A very small Cuban cigar.

Tag Stick
Wooden stick sharpened on one end and split about three inches on the other used to retain basket tickets on leaf warehouse sales floor.

Tagarnina

Cuban term indicating any inferior, bitter or fast-burning cigar.

Tailor-made

Slang, especially of the prisons, for machine-made cigarette, where hand rolled cigarettes are referred to as makin's.

Taking out a Barn

In flue-cured areas, removing the cured tobacco from the barn.

Tamoi

An Indian term used in Guiana to describe a variety of *Nicotiana Tabacum.*

Target

A form of rolled tobacco in which the roll is coiled into a flat layer. It is pressed and baked to a hard glossy black surface. It is used for either chewing or smoking tobacco, depending upon the type of leaf contained. Popular in Britain.

Tax - Federal

The first Federal tax on cigarettes was imposed in 1864 as a means of securing revenue after the Civil War. In its first year of enforcement the tax netted only $15,000, but the rate has been increased from eight tenths of a cent per package of twenty cigarettes to eight cents a pack (Nov. 1, 1951) and in 1952 yielded $1,474,000,000 on cigarettes alone.

Tax - State

Between 1921 and 1951 forty-one states enacted tax laws affecting cigarettes. The first of these were the agricultural states west of the Mississippi River.

Ten-centers

Economy cigarettes produced and sold during the 1930's.

Ten-pack

Trade term for a package of ten cigars, a recent innovation in the cigar industry. Only popular-priced cigars are sold in ten-pack units or, occasionally and very recently, in twenty-pack units.

Tenon

The projecting part of a tobacco pipe stem which fits into

the shank with which it forms a joint. In France, the Floc.

Tent

The cloth covering under which Connecticut Shadegrown wrapper tobaccos are raised.

TEPP

(*Tetraethyl pyrophosphate*). A chemical used extensively as an insecticide in flue-cured tobacco areas. This preparation is especially dangerous to handle and should be used with caution.

Tercio

A bale of Cuban tobacco tightly wrapped in *Yaguras* or the bark of the royal palm. A *tercio* contains an indefinite weight. Both weight and the number of leaves depend on the quality of the contents and the number of leaves which are tied in the hands or *manojos*. Bales of Semi-Vuelta leaf generally weigh about one hundred and twenty pounds or about one hundred and fifty pounds if of Remedios leaf. Tercios of Vuelta Abajo leaf generally contain eight *manojos*.

Therapeutic Use

Tobacco was long considered a panacea for physical ills, especially in Europe during the sixteenth and seventeenth centuries, earning such a name as *Herba Panacea*. *See* Smoking Tobacco and Cancer of the Lung.

Thin

A trade term referring to the shape of a small, thin cigar with a straight-cut tuck end. The thin is not as small as a cigarillo but much smaller and thinner than a corona.

Thin-crop

Tobacco of the domestic cigar type which is thin to medium in body but which does not have the characteristics of seconds, or leaves grown near the ground. Consists chiefly of leaves grown near the center of the plant. Also referred to as bright, bright-crop, first-crop, crop or cutters.

Thin Leaf Grades

Dark air-cured and fire-cured tobacco of a thin to medium body and over 16" long; also Maryland tobacco of medium body. Such leaves are government classified as C-group. Also called Thins.

Thins

A term designating light or thin wrapper Broadleaf cigar tobaccos these are very silky, elastic, oily, ripe, firm, etc., and of a light uniform color. See Thin Leaf Grades.

Three Hundred One

A hybrid selection of domestic Cuban shadegrown wrapper tobacco developed for its resistance to the black shank disease and raised chiefly in the Florida-Georgia wrapper region.

Three Sucker

A variety of flue-cured tobacco. The plant is of medium height with closely spaced leaves which are medium broad and very long. This variety produces cigarette tobacco on two-thirds of the plant. When grown on light soils the cured leaf is a bright yellow-orange, but when grown on more fertile soils may be of a dark orange.

Threshing

see GRINDING

Thrips

1) Local Connecticut Valley term for the sand flea.

2) A very small brownish insect which causes the damage known as "white veins," indicating the white bands extending along the midrib and main veins of affected leaves.

Through Price

The flat price paid for a crop of Pull-off (Straight-stripped) cigar tobacco.

Tie

1) In Bright Leaf areas, to make bundles of uncured leaf and tie them with twine.

2) To lay several leaves of cured tobacco together into hands and tie these "hands" with a strong binding leaf.

Tie Leaf

The leaf used to wrap the stems of a hand of cured tobacco. Also called a tier (ty-er).

Tier

A row or layer of tobacco in the curing barn.

Tier poles or Tier rails

The poles which hold the sticks of tobacco in the barn. They are placed 22 to 26 inches apart, one above the other.

Tierce

Part of a hogshead; nominally one-third. Also a forty-eight inch length hogshead.

Tipping

Removing tips from bundles of tobacco.

Tips

In flue-cured tobacco, the better leaves from near the top of the plant. Also called Bright Tips and distinguished from green tips, which are not used in the manufacture of cigarettes. In fire-cured tobaccos, also called Short Tips.

In Burley and Maryland tobaccos, tips normally consist of relatively narrow, sharp pointed, and heavy bodied leaves, under 16" long, usually grow on the top or upper part of the plant.

Tirilla

The band placed inside each box of genuine Havana cigars which reads "Genuine Havana cigars" in Spanish, English, French and German. See HAVANA.

Tobacco

A member of a large family of plants (the *Solanaceae*) which also includes the Irish potato, the tomato, belladonna, and nightshade. Of the genus *Nicotiana* there are several species. *N. rustica* was native to North America, but until *N. Tabacum* was introduced the production of tobacco proved unprofitable. Many varieties of tobacco have been introduced to the market, and to a certain extent hybrids have been developed which will show remarkable resistance to one or more kinds of disease, but the tobacco grown in this country is generally divided into types, including wrapper (U.S. types 61, 62), binder (U.S. types 51, 52, 53, 54, 55), filler (U.S. type 32) leaf. Burley, now used with other tobacco for blending in cigarettes is classified as U.S. type 31. Dark tobaccos, fire-cured and air-cured, include U.S. types 21, 22, 23, 24, and 35, 36, 37. Flue-cured tobaccos comprise the majority of varieties used in the cigarette industry and are classified as U.S. types 11, 12, 13, 14. Government classification of tobacco types, grades and standards has done much in recent years to stabilize the tobacco grades sold at market. There are at present about 26 standard commercial types of leaf defined by the Department of Agriculture.

The production of leaf-tobacco has become highly specialized, and each locale supplies the type of leaf which proves most favorable to its own weather and soil conditions. These factors therefore determine the kind of tobacco produced in a given area. Since the general conditions may vary considerably within a radius of a few miles, the larger division by types is broken down into "classes." Each type and class will have its own distinguishable grades which generally refer to the position of the leaf on the stalk as well as to its condition.

Tobacco was brought from the New World to the Old. It was "discovered," with the New World, in 1492. Sailors, adventurers and envoys quickly spread the novel herb and it was soon adopted in Africa, in Russia, on the Continent, in China, Japan, the Philippines, and India. (*See* SMOKING).

Tobacco as exchange

In the Chesapeake region tobacco was, in the early days, the accepted medium of exchange. Fees and debts were paid in cured leaf, to mechanic and minister alike.

When prospective wives arrived at Jamestown in 1619 their passage was paid for by one hundred and twenty pounds of Virginia leaf. *See* CLERGY.

Tobacco Beetle

An insect which attacks inside stores of all types of tobacco products, eating into fine Turkish tobaccos, cigars, pressed cake, etc. The egg of the tobacco beetle is white, about one-sixteenth inches long and yellowish-white. It generally lies in a curved position, and the body is covered with long yellowish-brown hairs to which particles of tobacco adhere. The adult is dull orange or mahogany color with a small head bent nearly at right angles to the body. The largest is about a tenth of an inch in diameter. Also commonly called Cigarette Beetle.

Tobacco Chart

Inexpensive and often inaccurate maps sold between 1840 and 1890 at any ships' chandlers. These were presumably called Tobacco Charts because of their stained brown appearance or because they could be bought at the price of an ounce of tobacco or for an ounce of tobacco.

Tobacco, History of

Tobacco was destined to become one of the greatest factors in Europeanizing the newly discovered continent and, according to many writers of that day, in barbarizing the Europeans. In keeping with its early religious use (see Smoking), the use of tobacco spread like a new faith and proved as impossible to stamp out.

Among the European nations Portugal was perhaps most influential in spreading the use of tobacco. In the latter fifteenth century Portugal was a rich and powerful country. Lisbon, its chief port, was the center of trade and commerce and busy with many adventurers and much talk of new lands to the West. Portuguese sailors were among the first in the Orient and Occident as well to discover, collect and pass tobacco on to those with whom they came into contact.

It is not surprising that the man who was most instrumental in bringing tobacco to central Europe was a French ambassador to the court at Lisbon—Jean Nicot of Nîmes. Nicot had been sent to arrange a marriage between the young King Sebastian and Henry II's daughter, Marguerite de Valois. Though failing in this mission, he became interested in a plant which was said to have amazing curative powers. He not only succeeded in starting tender seedlings but sent cuttings to the Cardinal of Lorraine, to the Cardinal's brother, the Grand Prior, and even to the Queen Mother, Catherine de Medici. Soon the plant was popular as the *Herbe du Grand Prieur* and the *Herbe de la Reine* or merely as *Herbe Panacea*. In 1570 the Liébault brothers, in their *L'Agriculture et la maison rustikue,* called it *Nicotiana,* which proved the more lasting appellation.

Diplomatic friendships among courtiers were no less effective in spreading the fame and the use of tobacco than were the more casual friendships of sailors in port.

Once introduced into a country, tobacco created its own demand. The chief ambassadors were the sailors and merchants who were sure to take a bountiful supply with them wherever they went. English ships carried the herb to the Baltic and into the North Sea, the Turks to the Black Sea, the Spanish to Italy and the Philippines, the Dutch to Scandinavia and the Cape of Good Hope, and the Dutch and Portuguese to India. Perhaps the greatest boost given to the tobacco habit was the Thirty-Years War. Soldiers from most parts of the continent and England shared the pleasures of smoking and carried it back to their native lands, just as travellers in Spain and France took the habit to Italy, Poland and Austria.

In most countries, however, the habit met with instant resistance from church and state. As with most matters, the habit throve under persecution and spread despite edict. By the seventeenth century all populated regions in Europe and the Near East as well as many areas of India, Japan, China and Africa were acquainted with tobacco and used it widely. See Russia, Turkey, Italy, Austria, Switzerland, China, Japan, United States, France and England. *See* SMOKING.

Tobacco in corda
see ROLL

Tobacco-Money
The use of tobacco as money was common in the South. As far back as 1619 it was used in Jamestown by bachelors to redeem their brides. However it also had its difficulties. Debtors and creditors would speculate, since it was more convenient to pay when the price of tobacco was low than when it was high, and this habit led to extreme uncertainty in business matters.

Tobacco Moth

(*Ephestia elutella* Hbn.). This pest has, in the last few years, become the most serious threat to stored flue-cured and oriental cigarette tobaccos. The larva, about three-eighths inches long, light pinkish brown, with rows of brown spots on its back, attacks unmanufactured stores of tobacco of high sugar content.

Tobacco Nation

A North American Indian Tribe also known as the Tionontati. When the French visited them in 1616 they were located south of Nottaioasaga Bay, in Ontario, and had so many large tobacco fields, that the French called them the "Tobacco Nation." They were of Iroquoisan linguistic stock.

Tobacco notes

Warehouse receipts (in Virginia from 1713 on) containing a statement as to the quality of the tobacco. Such "notes" became a medium of exchange in place of the actual tobacco some time after the Civil War.

Tobacco Shed

The shed in which Connecticut wrapper and other air-cured tobaccos are cured. The shed differs from the barn in being generally larger and providing more (controlled) ventilation.

Tobacco Storm

Weather sufficiently damp to "order" or soften cured cigar tobacco into a pliable form and put it "into case." *See* CASE.

Tobacco War

During the Revolutionary War the export of tobacco became an active concern for the British. Phillips, Arnold and Cornwallis destroyed some ten thousand hogsheads between 1789 and 1781. Their action is sometimes referred to as the Tobacco War.

Tobacco Wilt

see BACTERIAL WILT.

Tobaco

Francesco Hernandes, a Spanish physician, is believed to have brought a present of some tobacco to Philip the Second.

Tobaco is the name which he gave the herb. Oviedo (*Historia General de las Indias*, 1535) claimed that the implement which the Indians used for smoking was called *tobaco*, a sort of hollow forked cane. The forked-ends were inserted in the nostrils, the other end applied to the burning leaves.

Tobaco de exportacion

Cuban leaf grown in the Remedios district. As the name indicates, most of the tobacco raised in this district is exported as leaf.

Tobaco de liga

Blending tobacco raised in the Remedios district of Cuba. One of Cuba's chief tobacco exports.

Tobago

It has been said that the name *tobacco* is derived from this island, which was discovered by Columbus during his third voyage in 1498 and named, according to one story, after the pipe which the natives there were reported to have been using. Another account indicates that tobacco was named after this island because it resembled in shape a Carib pipe.

Tobah

Sir Francis Drake, in *The World Encompassed* (1628), spoke of the herb Tobah which the natives brought his ship as presents, "or indeed for sacrifices, upon this persuasion that we were gods."

Toby

A stogie. A kind of long, cheap cigar (slang).

Tongas

1) The poorest grade of Turkish tobacco leaves, loose and unsorted and taken from the bottom of the plant.

2) Bales of Turkish tobacco containing loosely packed graded leaves of selected quality. Such bales, covered with paper and burlap, weigh sixty or seventy pounds.

Tonka (tonqua) Bean

The seed of a fruit grown mostly in Venezuela which is used for flavoring chewing tobacco. After removal from the pod the seeds are soaked in strong rum, which causes the formation of coumarin crystals. After shipping the beans are again soaked according to a special formula and the resultant liquid is sprayed on tobaccos.

See FLAVOR.

Toombak

The tobacco, from Persia, which is used in the *nargileh* or *Sheesheh*. It is carefully washed before use and placed in the pipe bowl while still damp. Live coals are placed on top to ignite the leaves.

Topdressing

Applying fertilizer after the crop is transplanted in the field. A term of use mostly in the flue-cured areas.

Topper

Device used for mechanically closing cartons.

Topping

Removing blossoms and sometimes the top leaves in order to permit greater growth of desirable leaves.

In general topping, which prevents the development of the seedhead and directs the energies of the plant to the leaves, tends to increase the size, thickness, body and nicotine content of the leaves, especially on the upper part of the stalk.

Tops

In the trade, air-cured leaf that might be used as cigar binders.

Torcedor

Cuban cigar-maker, the skilled worker who selects the wrapper leaf suitable to the different types of cigar and insures the proper distribution of the filler leaves within the binder.

Torcido

A Cuban cigar made from twisted or rolled filler and a binder which serves also as a wrapper.

Tornabuona

In the latter part of the sixteenth century an envoy to France, Tornabuona, had sent tobacco plants to his native Italy. These were promptly named after him, though the term was not long in use,

Torquetts

A roll or twist of Perique tobaccos.

Toscani

A style of Italian cigar, black, long, slender, tapering, with a strong aroma made entirely from domestic fire-cured tobaccos. The Toscani was popular in the early emigrant days.

Trabisond

Turkish tobacco grown in the northernmost section of that country on the edge of the Black Sea. Used chiefly for blending pipe tobaccos.

Tragacanth

A gum used to hold the flag of the wrapper of a cigar.

Transfer Buyer

Originally a buyer who purchased less than a full hogshead of tobacco from a farmer and transferred it to full ones. Such buyers sold to the Burley market in Maryland until the late 1930's.

Trash

In Burley Tobacco "trash" is the second grade of leaves; i.e., the leaves which grow just over the "flyings" and next to the "lugs." Trash has come to have great value as a cigarette tobacco.

Tray

The particular tray used by the catcher at the cigarette-making machine. Each tray holds four thousand cigarettes as they come out of the machine.

Trece

(Thirteenth). A classification of large but defective shade-grown wrapper leaf grown in the Vuelta Abajo district in Cuba.

Triangulares

Frontmark for a cigar which is similar in shape to the Corona, but a full inch or more shorter. Bundles of these cigars are placed in triangular molds which give them the distinctive shape for which they are named. *See* FRONTMARK.

Trichi

(Short for "Trichinopoly"). A cheroot made in India (slang).

Trichinopoly

A "strong" type of cheroot made in India, chiefly around Madras.

Trigo

Literally, wheat, a strong yellow cigarette paper used in Cuba.

Trinidade

A name for a popular tobacco grown in Trinidad.

Tripa

Literally, filler, the Cuban term for the body of the cigar which is wrapped in the binder and wrapper.

Tripas de Banco

The term indicating small or defective wrapper leaves used as bench filler.

Truckers

Warehousemen who push duckbills.

Trunk

A box containing two hundred and fifty cigars which are molded into a square shape by the slight pressure exerted when the lid of the box is closed. There are twenty-five cigars to each row in a trunk, and wooden partitions separate each row.

Trust

The largest tobacco trust in this country was broken up in 1890 into the American Tobacco, Liggett & Myers, R. J. Reynolds, and the P. Lorillard companies. Tobacco companies have for many years been the chief target of antitrust legislation.

Tub

Container for cut filler.

Tube

The earliest form of the tobacco pipe was a slender, straight, hollow cylinder with a pebble at one end to prevent the inhalation of tobacco dust.

Tuck
The lighting end of a cigar.

Tuck Cutter
A stationary knife attached to a block of wood, used for cutting the "tuck" of a cigar.

Tucks
Small pieces of tobacco cut from the ends of cigars. Cuttings and tucks are bought by scrap chewing manufacturers or cigar makers and are used either as scrap filler or in the production of scrap filler.

see CUTTINGS

Tumblin's
Tobacco for a pipe or cigarette (slang).

Turkey
Tobacco was introduced into Turkey in the middle of the sixteenth century through English, Dutch, Spanish and Italian trade with that country. Tobacco quickly spread, along with the use of coffee, but had the misfortune to meet with the displeasure of the Ottoman ruler, Murad the Cruel. Murad, at special pains to stamp out the habit, blamed a local uprising in 1633 on the smokers who congregated in smoking dens and aired their objectionable political views. Smoking was declared a violation of the precepts of the *Koran*. The offence of smoking was punishable by death, though the charge may have had a rather liberal interpretation depending on the political affiliations of the accused, for the sadistic Sultan is said to have dispatched as many as twenty-five thousand victims in the last five years of his reign. Murad's technique did not succeed, however, in stamping out the smoking of tobacco. The situation was in time alleviated by the succession of the less violent Ibrahim and the introduction of snuff. With Turkey's defeat in 1683 and the reign of Mohammed IV smoking was legalized and the growth of tobacco encouraged.

Turkish
A general class of tobaccos raised in Turkey and contiguous territories. Such tobacco is nearly always air-cured. It is di-

vided into two types: *yaka* or upland, tobacco and *ova,* that which is raised on the lowlands. Tobaccos of the various regions differ greatly in their characteristic flavours and qualities and are imported mostly for blending with domestic leaf.

Turning

Cured shadegrown tobacco which has been tied in hands is piled in large "bulks" with about three thousand to five thousand pounds in each pile. The tobacco is sweated in bulk and must be turned every eight or ten days so that the outside hands form the inside or core of a new bulk where they will be subject to the most intense heat of the fermentation or sweating process.

Turning the Ticket

The farmer who rejected the warehouse bid would so signify by turning the record face down or tearing the coupon half-way across.

Also termed "Tuck the Ticket."

Turtle Foot

A variety of dark-fired Virginia tobacco with long leaves of medium width and good curing qualities.

Twenty grand

A package of cigarettes (slang).

Twist

1) A cigar shaped into a twist made by twisting three cigars together to form one turned or twisted shape. The three are of course separated before smoking, but each retains its peculiar crooked shape.

2) A form of chewing tobacco very much like roll, made, usually by hand in small factories, by twisting stemmed leaf into small rolls which are folded. One-Sucker, Burley and fire-cured types are used.

Twist a dizzy or dream

Roll a cigarette (slang).

Twist One

Slang, especially of the underworld, for rolling a cigarette by hand. Synonymous with "roll a pill," "fix makin's," etc.

Two-girl machine
  see SCRAP FILLER MACHINE
Two-Penny Act of 1755
  see CLERGY
Twofer
  Trade term for an old-fashioned two-for-a-nickel scrap-filled cigar.
Twentieth
  A trade term for cigars sold in lots of fifty, these being one twentieth of one thousand, the unit upon which the original price is reckoned. Thus "a fortieth" refers to twenty-five cigars.
Type
  A subdivision of class of leaf; that is, any tobacco that has the same characteristics and corresponding qualities, colors and lengths.
Tyrolian pipe
  A wood pipe favored by Austrian peasants and mountaineers, generally made from local wood and characterized by the long vertical shank and right-angled round bit, usually made of bone. The bowl itself which is covered with a small ventilated top drops to chest height and is usually supported by the smoker's free hand. The shank may be made from a prunis wood or from more expensive and finely carved woods.

U

Undried

The condition of unfermented tobacco which has not been airdried or steamdried.

Uniformity

By government definition, one of the elements of quality in tobacco, having reference to the consistency of a lot as ordinarily sorted and prepared for market. Uniform tobacco deviated less than 10% per lot.

Unit

Trade term for the number of ounces of tobacco required to make a given number of cigars. In some cases the unit is figured by number rather than by weight.

United States

The story of tobacco in this country begins with pre-Colonial times, for the herb was in use among North American Indian tribes for ceremonial and medicinal purposes. Its modern history however, begins (ironically enough with the settlement named after the most determined anti-tobacconist of all the English monarchs) when John Rolfe brought to the Jamestown Settlement some of the plants he had collected in the West Indies. During a brief and rather accidental sojourn in the Bermudas Rolfe had gathered seeds of *Nicotiana tabacum*, a strain which quickly replaced the tough *Nicotiana rustica* and permitted the first extensive cultivation of the tobacco plant. Rolfe himself, by his marriage to Pocahontas, helped ensure sufficient peace for the struggling community so that crops could be grown with some assurance of harvest. The yield of 1618 was twenty-thousand pounds, but by 1623 the first of a series of trade agreements was reached which insured the colonies a steady market for the export of tobacco.

Exports from Virginia before 1700 increased from five hundred thousand pounds in 1628 to eighteen million, one hundred fifty-seven thousand pounds in 1688, and large quantities were also produced in Maryland during this period. Efforts to stabilize the price through crop control were instituted as early as 1629, and the following year tobacco became a legal medium of exchange in Virginia. James I's prohibition against the growth of tobacco in England further stimulated the export trade in the Colonies. Virginia and Maryland continued to produce the greater share of tobacco throughout the eighteenth century, but after the Revolutionary War tobacco culture spread to Ohio, Kentucky, Tennessee and Missouri.

By the close of the century tobacco production from all sources topped eight hundred million pounds per year. While Virginia was required to ship all her tobacco to England, Maryland was free to export to the continent, and France and the Netherlands were principal buyers.

The cigar industry in this country began in Connecticut at the end of the eighteenth century, and the first cigar factories were opened about 1810. The cigar-leaf industry did not assume great commercial importance, however, until the middle of the nineteenth century. By 1889 over eighty-six thousand pounds of cigar-leaf tobaccos were produced in the seven principal states, and by 1899 over one hundred seventy thousand five hundred pounds. By this time more than five billion cigars were produced in the country, while imports, during the later years mostly from Cuba, reached a peak of one hundred million.

After the turn of the century the tobacco industry made enormous advances, especially in the production of blended cigarettes. The production of all types of tobaccos has advanced, since 1900, to more than two billion pounds per annum.

In 1949 the United States produced 27.4 percent of the world's tobacco. Of this amount nearly 38 percent was produced in North Carolina, and 22 percent in Kentucky. South Carolina, Virginia and Tennessee each produced 7 percent,

Georgia nearly 6 percent, Pennsylvania 3 percent, Maryland just over 2 percent, and Wisconsin 1.6 percent.

For classification, see TOBACCO. For history see SMOKING.

Unsound

By government specifications, tobacco under 20% damaged.

Unstemmed

A form of leaf tobacco consisting of a collection of leaves from which the stems or midribs have not been removed, including leaf scraps.

Uppowoc

In *A Briefe and True Report of the New Found Land of Virginia* (1588), Ralfe Lane, the governor, wrote of *uppowoc,* the herb which the Indians grow apart and the Spaniards call *Tobacco.* "The leaves thereof being dried and brought into powder, they use to take the fume or smoke thereof by sucking it through pipes made of clay into their stomache and heade, from whence it purgeth superfluous flame and other grosse humours . . . (and) not only perserveth the body from obstructions, but also if any be so that they have beene of too long continuance, in short time breaketh them."

Urea

A chemical sold as Uramon used to destroy both weeds and soil borne diseases such as root knot and black root rot. Frequently used in combination with cyanamide. Urea also acts as a high-nitrogen fertilizer.

Utz

Top leaves of the Basma plant. The smallest and highest leaves.

V

Vaal
see FALLOW.

Vamorr Forty-eight
A hybrid variety of flue-cured tobacco developed for its resistance to mosaic and root rot. The plant is of medium height, the leaves smooth, broad, and somewhat rounded and spaced medium close on the stalk.

Variegated
By government definition, tobacco having a diversity of contrasting colors or tints, other than green, within a leaf; or leaves which are in part distinctly gray, mottled, bleached, stained or doty-faced; or leaves which in part have been badly discolored in the curing process by scalding, scorching, etc. Also leaves which do not blend with the colors established for the type, or a lot of tobacco containing 30% or more of variegated leaves.

Vega
A Cuban tobacco field. Each vega is an independent unit, physically and economically. The term itself refers to river bottom lands and to preferred tobacco land or "tabacal." A group of *Vegas* are called a *Veguerio*.

Vegetable Weevil
An insect (larva and adult form) attacking flue-cured tobaccos, eating irregular holes in the leaves, or the bud and entire leaf except the mid-rib.

Veguerio
see VEGA.

Vein Banding
A virus disease attacking tobacco plants. The disease causes narrow dark-green bands along veins and, especially in Florida,

marked retardation of younger leaves, dead spots on older leaves. Common to all tobacco areas; spread by aphids.

Velin

Rice paper used in making cigarette paper. Velin is distinguishable from Rayado and Verge in that it bears no water marks.

Verge

A type of rice paper used in making cigarette paper. Verge is distinguished by semi-transparent lines running crosswise. This paper weighs twenty to twenty-one grams to the square meter.

Vesta

Several varieties of this flue-cured tobacco have been bred. In each case they combine a black shank resistant strain with Warne and Yellow Special (as in Vestall, 26, 30 and 33) or with White Stem Orinoco and Yellow Special (as in Vesta 44, 46, 47, 52, 53, 55, 56, 62 and 64). The plants are of medium height, but may vary in shape of leaf and spacing, etc. Mature leaves are rich lemon to orange color when cured.

Vigo

A popular snuff in England, early in the 18th century. So called because it was part of the booty captured at Vigo, Spain, 1702.

Violet Strasburgh

One of the more popular snuffs of the eighteenth century, consisting of Rappee and bitter almonds, ambergris and attargul being added for scent. It was an especial favorite of the ladies of the continent and England.

Virginia Bright Leaf

One of the oldest varieties of flue-cured tobaccos, adaptable to variety of soil conditions. The plant grows to medium height with leaves spaced medium close together on the stalk. Bottom leaves are long and fairly broad, but the yield is about the lowest of all flue-cured varieties.

Virginia Fire-cured

Common name for one of the fire-cured tobaccos raised

principally in the Piedmont and mountain sections of Virginia. Government classified as Type 21 of Class 2.

Virginia Gold

A strong hybrid flue-cured tobacco of medium height and large stalk. The leaves have a tendency toward a yellowish cast, but may be cherry red. When cured they are rich lemon to orange in color.

Virginia Sun-cured

Common name for a type of air-cured tobacco grown principally in the central section of Virginia, north of James River. Government classified as Type 37 of Class 3. Formally the strain was exposed to the sun in the curing process, but now it is generally cured in the same manner as Burley tobacco.

Virginia Tobacco

Essentially a plug filler type, though some portion of the crop may be used for plug wrapper. It is generally cured in the same manner as Burley tobacco.

Another name for flue-cured or "Southern Bright" tobaccos.

Viso

A term which, especially in the Cuban tobacco trade, has reference to a copperish color in the leaf of certain cigar tobaccos.

Vitola

The frontmark or shape of a Cuban cigar. The Vitola is also the mold or the model or the shape and size of the cigar. The word was itself taken from the Spanish slang expression of American usage which indicated the mold used in ship construction. In one collection of vitolas in a Havana factory there are nine hundred ninety-six different types.

Vuelta Abajo

A district of Cuba producing the finest quality of leaf used for cigar wrappers and in the manufacture of Genuine Havanas. Much of the tobacco import from Havana comes from this region, which is located in the Pinar del Rio section of the Province of Pinar del Rio. *See* HAVANA.

W

Walliser cigar

A dark cigar, similar to the Toscani, *q.v.*

Walloon

A local name for tobacco mosaic. *See* MOSAIC.

Walnut

Dun flue-cured leaf. *See* DUN.

Water Balers

A highly processed tobacco produce made from One-Sucker or fire-cured leaves which are subject to a strong steaming while still tied in hands, then packed under pressure while still moist from further treatment. Sold almost exclusively to the West Indies and Central and South American markets.

Water Pipe, Oriental

Although perfect forms of the water pipe were found in Turkey and Persia in the sixteenth century, there is no proof that tobacco was smoked in them. Hemp was probably used. *See* NARGILEH and HOOKAH.

Web

1) By government definition, that portion of a leaf as distinguished from the stem or midrib, or that portion of a tobacco leaf from which the midrib has been removed.

2) Any lot of tobacco consisting of the web of leaves, or any unstemmed unmanufactured leaves except scrap.

Web- or Strip-Blend

By government definition, a group of tobacco which consists of the web or strips of closely related grades blended together in the stemming process.

Web-scrap

Stemmed scrap consisting of portions of strips.

Web-yield

The weight of clean web usable in tobacco products. Web-yield is normally expressed as a percentage of the original unstemmed weight.

Weed

Slang for tobacco or sometimes for cigarette. ("Gimme a weed!") In the underworld "weed" refers specifically to marijuana.

Weeding

see HOEING

Weight

see ACTUAL WEIGHT, MARKED WEIGHT AND RECEIVING WEIGHT

Wellington

A style of pipe which has a rounded bowl and a curved stem joined to the shank with a large ferrule. The stem has always a diamond-like shape, with its widest circumference near the ferrule. The bit is usually fashioned with a slight undercut; that is, it is of the "push" type.

West Indies

The commercial cultivation of tobacco by Europeans was initiated here in 1535 by the Spaniards. Also see UNITED STATES.

Western District Bright

Common name for one of the flue-cured tobaccos raised principally in the Piedmont sections of Virginia and North Carolina. Classified by government standards as Type 11 of Class 1.

Western District Dark

Common name for one of the fire-cured tobaccos produced principally in a section between the Tennessee, Ohio, and Mississippi Rivers in western Kentucky and northwestern Tennessee. Government classified as Type 23 of Class 1.

Western Fire-cured

Common name for one of the fire-cured tobaccos produced principally in a section between the Tennessee, Ohio, and Mississippi Rivers in western Kentucky and northwestern Tennessee. Government classified as Type 23 of Class 1.

Wet

1) By government specification, sound tobacco which is subject to damage because of dampness unless proper precautions are taken.

2) Leaf cured in high case is often termed wet, or moist.

Wet (Moist) Snuff

A snuff which in texture and aroma is more moist and sweeter than "dry" snuff; generally of the Rappee variety. In the manufacturing process tobacco leaves, stalks, and scrap are placed together in a wooden bin. Water or a saline solution is added and the "cure" or fermentation process begins. The temperature is allowed to rise to over one hundred and thirty degrees, and the cure may last more than three weeks. The resultant tobacco mass is removed from the brine and heaped into square wooden bins with a permitted amount of salt. When fully cured it is removed, flavorings are added, and the tobacco is hardened and pulverized.

see DRY SNUFF

Wet Weather Crops

Domestic cigar tobaccos raised under unusually humid atmospheric conditions cannot be processed for two, three, or more years after cutting. Pennsylvania tobacco cut in 1941 was not used until 1947 or 1948.

Wet Weather French

Colloquial term for Frenching, *which see.*

White Burley

In 1864 George Webb, of Higginsport, Ohio, set out Red Burley plants which soon appeared to sicken and become white. When grown and air-cured, the underside of these leaves appeared of a whitish tinge, while the upperside was golden yellow. Burley plants grown under these soil conditions and bearing a characteristic whitish tinge are commonly called White Burley. The leaf is generally large in size and of fine tissue.

The plant reaches its highest state of development in the bluegrass section of Kentucky, in the eastern Tennessee district, and in southern Ohio. It is best grown on virgin soil.

Soil preparation, sowing and seedbed care are about the same as for flue-cured tobaccos.

see BURLEY

White cigars

The English classification for cigars made from Havana or Virginia leaf, as opposed to the *black,* or those made of Brazilian tobacco.

White Stem Orinoco

One of the oldest of the flue-cured varieties. The plant does best on infertile soils, grows to medium height with leaves closely spaced on the stalk. Top leaves are somewhat narrow and, before topping, grow in an upright fashion.

Wildfire

Caused by *Pseudomonas tabaci* (Wolf & Foster). An infectious disease of the plant-bed which appears in spots within the plant bed, within which the center plants may have been destroyed. Yellow lesions appear on diseased leaves and usually a small white area of dead tissue in the center.

Wilt Stage

In "outdoor" tobaccos, the initial stage of the curing process during which the cut tobacco becomes limp and pliable. Artificial heat from charcoal or gas fires may be used at this time to control the curing of such air-cured tobaccos.

Wilting

A term generally applied to "outdoor" or Broadleaf and Havana Seed areas to indicate moistening the leaf so that it will not tear in handling, especially as it is "handed up" to the spearer or hooker.

Windrow

Flue-cured tobacco, when removed from the barn, is packed in the pack house in a long pile or windrow, where it may be left in such a condition for several days before further packing.

Wireworm

One of the larvae of various species of snapping beetles or daters; so-called from their slenderness and the hardness of their integument.

Wireworms attack tobacco plants promptly after they are set in the field, the resulting injury causing the plants to wilt and die or at least hampering normal growth.

Woodbine
Slang for a cheap cigar or cigarette.

Wooden Ear
A buyer who raises his own bid. The term is current in flue-cured areas.

Wooden Indians
The distinctive trade symbol of the tobacconist. Other figures such as Turks, Negroes, trappers and Jenny Lind were also popular. The use of such figures probably originated in England, where, as early as 1630, "blackmores" or carved black boys made their appearance. The National Geographic Society has estimated that in 1900 there were some 100,000 wooden Indians in the United States and that there are only 3,000 today.

Woodstock
A style of pipe with a funneling straight-sided bowl and curved stem and shank. This curve brings the bit up level with the top of the bowl. The style is similar to that of the Sickle, though the stem is not so curved.

Worming
Hand removal of tobacco horn worms from growing plants.

Wrap one up
Roll a cigarette (slang).

Wrapper
1) In cigar tobaccos, leaves selected for the outer wrapping of the cigar itself. The wrapper is the final leaf added, giving the cigar its characteristic color and controlling the rate of combustion. It is rolled around the bunch in a spiral, beginning at the end which is to be lighted—the "tuck." A small amount of vegetable gum holds the wrappers in place.

Wrappers are selected from either leaf or lugs, and must be silky, fairly oily, ripe, firm, strong and more elastic than leaf or lugs. They have bright finish, blending fibers and are almost perfect leaves.

2) Wrappers, among the trade, generally refer to top grade Pennsylvania leaf.

3) In flue-cured tobaccos, leaves that are almost perfect, selected from the leaf and cutter group.

Wrapper B's
Domestic air-cured tobaccos used for cigar filler purposes.

Wrapper Casing Machine
A patented device for ordering cigar wrapper leaf by means of moist air. Hands of leaves are fastened to large verticle revolving racks by means of a rubber clip. Moist air is blown onto the leaves as they pass over the top of the elliptical cylinder.

Wrapping
In flue-cured areas, attaching the leaves to sticks in preparation for curing.

Wringer
Machine for squeezing water from leaf tobacco.

X Y Z

Xanthi

Tobaccos raised near the town of Xanthi in eastern Greece are considered to be the finest of the Turkish blends used in smoking tobacco. This leaf, grown on a very small area south and west of the town is called Xanthi Yaka Basma. A second leaf, only slightly inferior to it is the Xanthi Ova Basma, grown along the coast of the Aegean Sea.

Yaka

see TURKISH

Yard of Clay

The nineteenth century English term for a clay pipe with a stem sufficiently long to permit the smoker to rest the bowl on the arm of his chair without bending over. Pipe and stem were in one piece. In the preceding century Yards of Clay were more commonly known as "Aldermen." Such pipes were especially favored by the British and Dutch.

Yarra

see MAYARI

Yellow

Virginia tobacco. The term was commonly used about 1890. In 1852 Eli and Elisha Slade planted tobacco on poor land between the two tributaries of the Dan River in Caswell County, N. C. When cured with charcoal fires the resulting yellow-colored leaf was found to be sweeter and more attractive than the then popular Sumatra-types. Sandy, infertile soil contributed to the color.

Yellow Hammer

A slang expression of the Bright Tobacco areas for anyone who speculates on the tobacco market, especially on low profit margins.

Yellow Mammoth

A flue-cured tobacco generally grown on sandy loam soils. The leaves, medium in width, are relatively close together on a medium height stalk. They cure to a rich lemon color.

Yellow Special

A popular flue-cured tobacco of medium height and broad leaves of a good length. The plant does well in a variety of soil conditions and has a moderate resistance to black root rot. When cured the leaves are usually a lemon color.

Yellowing

A term applied to the curing of flue and fire-cured tobaccos. Yellowing is the first stage of the curing process. During this time the temperature is slowly raised from eighty-five or ninety degrees to one hundred five or one hundred and ten degrees.

Yenitz

The District in Turkey, in the Province of Thrace, where tobacco was first grown, in the middle of the eighteenth century. Tobacco from this region is called Yenitz. Also termed Yenidge. This variety of Macedonian Turkish produces oval or lance-shaped leaves from two and a half to ten inches in length. It was perhaps more popular for export in the 18th century than it is now.

Yetl

The Nahuatlan word used in Mexico, meaning tobacco.

Yoli

The Indian term by which tobacco was known on parts of the South American continent before 1560.

York County Filler

Common name for a cigar-filler tobacco produced in York County of Pennsylvania. Government classification Class 4, Type 41.

York State Tobacco

Common name for a cigar-binder leaf produced principally in the Big Flats and Onondaga sections of New York and Pennsylvania. Government classified as Type 53. Another leaf of this type is called Havana Seed of New York.

Youly

The popular name used to designate any variety of tobacco, by the inhabitants of the Antilles.

Zanders

A natural variety of Pennsylvania Seedleaf which produces a good leaf shape and a high percentage of wrappers.

Zimmer Spanish

Common name for a Havana Seed tobacco produced principally in the Miami section of Ohio and used as a cigar filler. Government classification: Type 43.

Also called Ohio Zimmer and Zimmer.

Zineb

The active chemical in Dithane Z-78 and Parzate; a chemical specific for the control of blue mold in flue-cured crops.

Zorullo

Literally, a soft round object. The Cuban term for a poorly made cigar. Also the roll of filler for one cigar before the binder is added.

The Arctic
and
Antarctica

Roof and Floor of the World

Alice Gilbreath

d̶P DILLON PRESS, INC.
Minneapolis, Minnesota 55415

Library of Congress Cataloging-in-Publication Data

Gilbreath, Alice Thompson.
The Arctic and Antarctica : roof and floor of the world /
by Alice Gilbreath.
p. cm. — (Ocean world library)
Bibliography: p.
Includes index.
Summary: Describes various aspects of the Arctic and
Antarctica including the animals that live there, the people
who have explored them, and the changes brought to these
faraway regions by modern technology and the search for
new energy sources.
ISBN 0-87518-373-5 : $11.95
1. Polar regions—Juvenile literature. [1. Polar regions.]
I. Title. II. Series.
G590.G55 1988
998—dc 19   87-32448
                                                          CIP
                                                           AC

Dillon Press, Inc., 242 Portland Avenue South
Minneapolis, Minnesota 55415

Printed in the United States of America
4 5 6 7 8 9 10 97 96 95 94 93 92 91 90 89

To T'Alana,
Bryan, Daniel,
Laura, Michael,
and Sami Lynn

Acknowledgments

I am grateful to Wayne E. Smith, Lt. Col., USAF (retired) for checking this manuscript and for his helpful suggestions.

Photographic Acknowledgments

The photographs are reproduced through the courtesy of the Alaska Division of Tourism; Alaska News; *Department of the Navy, Office of Information (Robert Carlin, artist, and official U.S. Navy photographs by PH3 William R. Curtsinger, PH1 G.V. Graves, PH2 Carl H. Jackson, Sr., PH1 David B. Loveall, PH1 T. Milton Putnam, PH1 Paul L. Schlappich, PH2 J. Urciuoli, and PH1 Robert L. Ziesler); Jim Gasparini and Will Steger/Firth Photo Bank; National Archives; and Norwegian Information Service in the United States.*

Contents

 # Arctic and Antarctic Facts

Physical Makeup:

    Arctic—water surrounded by land

    Antarctic—land surrounded by water (about 5,100,000 square miles, or 13,209,000 square kilometers)

Average Temperatures:

    Arctic— -30°F (-34°C) in winter; 30°F (-1°C) in summer

    Antarctic— -40° to -80°F (-40° to -62°C) in winter; 32°F (0°C) in summer

Native Animals:

    Arctic—polar bear, caribou, reindeer, arctic fox, lemming, walrus, ringed seal

    Antarctic—leopard seal, Weddell seal, Adélie penguin, Emperor penguin, red krill

Native Peoples:

    Arctic—Inuit, Lapps, Zyrians, Evenks, Yakuts, Tungus, Nenets, Chukchis, Koryaks, Kamchadals

    Antarctic—none

Location of the Poles:

    North Pole—90° latitude north, in the Arctic

    South Pole—90° latitude south, in Antarctica

Months of Constant Daylight:
> *North Pole*—March to September
> *South Pole*—September to March

Months of Constant Darkness:
> *North Pole*—September to March
> *South Pole*—March to September

First to Reach the North Pole:
> *By dogsled*—Dr. Frederick A. Cook (April 21, 1908) or
> Admiral Robert E. Peary (April 6, 1909)
> *By plane*—Admiral Richard E. Byrd (May 9, 1926)
> *By submarine*—Commander William Anderson and
> crew of the *Nautilus* (August 3, 1958)

First North Pole Expedition (Dogsled) to Include a Woman:
Ann Bancroft, Steger International Polar Expedition
(May 1, 1986)

First to Reach the South Pole:
> *By dogsled*—Roald Amundsen (December 16, 1911)
> *By plane*—Admiral Richard E. Byrd (November 29,
> 1929)

Strangely shaped ice formations rise from McGregor Glacier in Antarctica.

The Ends of the Earth

Huge **glaciers*** thousands of feet deep, towering cliffs of moving ice, thundering **icebergs** the size of Connecticut—all form part of the rugged beauty and vast open spaces of the Arctic and Antarctica. The ends of the earth are places where extremes are normal, where for months at a time day and night never end. They are distant, hidden, changing places that have challenged and fascinated the people who have lived in or explored them.

Imagine what it would be like to travel to the top and bottom of the world—the **North Pole** and the **South Pole**. Early in the twentieth century, daring explorers, traveling by dogsled, first reached the Poles. Since then a number of other explorers have made similar journeys over the ice, and many others have traveled there by plane. In the 1950s a nuclear-powered submarine, the *Nautilus*, made the first undersea (and ice) trip to the North Pole. Today, the United States maintains the Amundsen-Scott South Pole re-

*Words in **bold type** are explained in the glossary at the end of this book.

search station, where nineteen people live year round.

The North and South Poles lie far within the most remote and least known regions on earth. Both the Arctic and Antarctica are extremely cold, ice-covered areas that test the survival skills of people and animals. Yet in many ways the "roof" and "floor" of the world are different.

Much of the Arctic is a moving, frozen ocean of sea ice, which borders the northernmost parts of Asia, Europe, and North America. Antarctica is a continent, covered in most places by an **ice cap** more than a mile (1.6 kilometers) deep, and surrounded by ocean waters and currents. In some places high mountains and valleys rise above the level of the immense ice cap. Parts of the Arctic change from sea ice to open ocean during the short arctic spring and summer. During this brief season, snow disappears from large areas of arctic land. Flowers bloom, insects and birds fill the sky, and animals roam among the ponds and lakes of the "arctic prairie." Almost all of Antarctica remains ice-covered throughout the year, although some of the ice does melt in the surrounding ocean. Sea mammals and birds in the sea and coastal areas are the only animals of any size that live in the antarctic region.

People have lived in the Arctic for thousands of years, and have adapted to the bitterly cold climate and long, dark winters. They settled mainly in the coastal areas, where they could fish and hunt seals and whales. Some groups settled inland, where they hunted wild caribou or herded reindeer. Wherever the arctic people lived, they made their clothes from animal skins and followed the rhythm of the seasons.

After the early explorers reached the North Pole, people from the "south" began to take more of an interest in the lands of the far north. During World War II, nations built military bases in the Arctic, and the region has since become an area vital to the forward defenses of the United States and the Soviet Union. In the 1960s and 1970s, the discovery of oil and the building of the Alaska pipeline brought thousands of workers to Alaska's North Slope. Valuable deposits of coal, iron, and other minerals have also been developed in areas throughout the Arctic. The newcomers and the modern ways they brought with them caused rapid changes in the lives of the native arctic peoples.

Until nations established modern research stations in Antarctica, no one lived there in a permanent settlement. Scientists followed, or accompanied, the

early explorers, and today Antarctica has become the site of a variety of important scientific research. As in the Arctic, oil and other minerals lie beneath the coastal waters and ice-covered land. Yet, because of cooperation among a group of nations with research stations there, Antarctica remains the last undeveloped and unspoiled continent on earth.

Why are people attracted to these faraway places where cold, wind, ice, and snow make life itself a constant challenge? For some, the chance to explore one of the world's last frontiers is reason enough to make such a long, difficult journey. For others, the opportunity to work or to conduct research in a remote, beautiful, and peaceful area of the world has a strong appeal. For everyone who travels to the Arctic and Antarctica, the experience is an adventure—for many the adventure of a lifetime.

A native Alaskan.

The Roof of the World

If you stood at the North Pole, deep within the vast region of arctic ice, you would be looking down from the top of the earth. From the North Pole, there is no north, east, or west. There is only south.

Several million square miles of water form the **Arctic Ocean**—the roof of the world. Here, the world's northernmost ocean borders the northern fringes of Alaska, Canada, Greenland, Norway, Sweden, Finland, and the Soviet Union. Much of the ocean's surface water is frozen in layers of sea ice.

Some of the arctic ice has remained frozen for centuries. As new ice forms under the old, the top layer heaves upward, cracking the surface. Huge chunks break off. These broken pieces of floating ice are called **ice floes**. They bang against each other and freeze together. After cracking and breaking and refreezing many times, ice floes are stacked in some places like hills. Such ice hills are filled with large caves and steep cliffs that make them difficult to cross.

This map of the Arctic shows the region with the North Pole at its center.

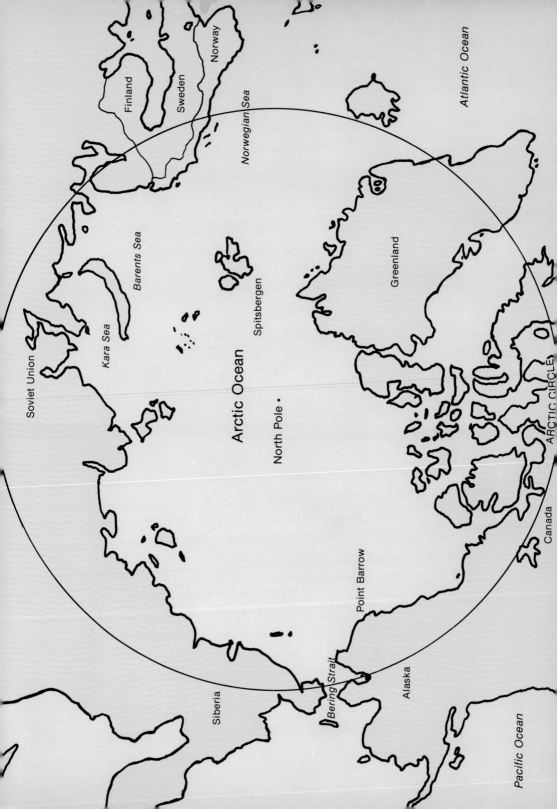

Ice floes in the Arctic Ocean.

In the Arctic Ocean, currents of water flow beneath the ice. Most of these currents are cold. One, the **Gulf Stream**, carries warmer water from an area of the Atlantic Ocean far to the south.

An ice cap is a very large mass of ice, called a glacier, which forms when snow packs so solidly that it becomes ice. Part of Greenland is covered by an ice cap thousands of feet deep.

Icebergs on the Move

Most arctic icebergs form at the edge of an ice cap. The weight of such an enormous glacier causes it to move slowly downward. When the glacier, moving a few inches each day, reaches the ocean, large pieces at the edge—icebergs—break off.

An iceberg, which is many times higher than a large ship, floats in the ocean because it is lighter than ocean water. Since icebergs are formed from fresh water—rain or snow—they do not contain salt. The lack of salt makes an iceberg lighter than the salty ocean water that supports its weight.

What we see of an iceberg is only a tiny part of it. Only about one-eighth of an iceberg extends above the water. The far larger, underwater part can cause great harm to ocean-going vessels. Icebergs have damaged and sunk many ships, including the *Titanic*, which sank in 1912. Icebergs such as the one hit by the *Titanic* may last for three years and melt when they drift south into the much warmer waters of the Gulf Stream.

Icebergs often form in the spring, when the arctic ice begins to melt. Then, ships can travel through parts of the Arctic Ocean. In September, this ocean again

Most icebergs break off from the edge of an ice cap, and they may float through the ocean for months or years.

begins to freeze. Soon tiny ice crystals cover the water. As they freeze into a solid sheet, fields of sea ice form at the surface. Below the surface, the ice becomes thicker and thicker. In one year, it may become eight or nine feet (2.4 to 2.7 meters) thick. Ice that does not completely melt during the summer months may form a rock-hard layer fifteen feet (4.6 meters) thick within a few years.

Arctic Weather—Day and Night

Throughout much of the year, the arctic region stays extremely cold. In some parts, temperatures drop to -80°F (-62°C). Yet, the temperatures alone do not provide an accurate picture of how severe this cold can become. Wind, combined with these low temperatures, creates conditions that threaten the lives of people who explore this vast area of ice and snow. Storms may come up suddenly. Dense fogs often reduce **visibility** to a few yards.

The **arctic whiteout** is another hazard for those who travel here. When clouds are thick in the sky and the ground is covered with snow, a traveler cannot tell where the sky stops and the snow begins. An object that appears to be close by may actually be miles away.

Because of the earth's **rotation**, or spin, the arctic ice moves all the time. Slowly, it drifts clockwise from Alaska and Siberia toward Greenland. And since the earth tilts to one side as it spins, the North Pole sometimes points toward the sun and sometimes away from it.

During the spring and the summer months, the Arctic tilts toward the sun. Then, at the exact top of the

world, the sun never sets. For six months, it shines twenty-four hours a day. During the fall and winter months, when the North Pole tilts away from the sun, there are six months of darkness. In arctic areas to the south of the Pole, the periods of total daylight and darkness last for less than six months.

During the long arctic night, sometimes the sky brightens with flickering lights or a steady glow of bands of pale light. These moving light beams, tinged with red, yellow, green, or violet, are known as the **aurora borealis**, or northern lights.

Since part of the Arctic is frozen all year, people did not discover until this century that most of it is an ocean. Along the edges of the ocean, though, lies a huge area of treeless land that supports a great variety of animals and plants.

Spring and Summer in the Arctic

The white coat that the Arctic has worn all winter changes suddenly in the spring. Snow begins to disappear on the **tundra**—the land bordering the Arctic Ocean and reaching south to the edge of the northern forests.

The Tundra Comes Alive

The tundra, sometimes called the "arctic prairie," covers one-tenth of the earth's land surface. In the spring, after a very long winter, cracks appear in the ice at the edge of the ocean. The ice and snow of the tundra melt, leaving pools. Since **permafrost**, the permanently frozen subsoil beneath the pools, is as hard as rock, this melted water has no place to go.

Soon, mosses and **lichens**—tiny plants that are a combination of algae and fungi—begin to grow. The arctic sky fills with birds that **migrate** to the north from southern areas where they live during winter months. Geese, loons, swans, and plovers appear.

Some have come from as far away as Florida. The arctic tern flies an incredible 11,000 miles (17,700 kilometers) from Antarctica to its arctic breeding grounds. The birds jostle and fight as they search for food and places to build nests.

Sparrow-sized snow buntings arrive after a 3,000-mile (4,830-kilometer) journey. Males come first to select nesting sites. Females arrive three weeks later. The Arctic is an excellent place for buntings to nest because they find an abundant supply of mosquitoes to feed their young.

Eggs of mosquitoes and flies have been frozen all winter. During the spring, these eggs hatch, and insects fill the air. Even though birds eat many of them, the sky remains full of insects.

As the great thaw continues, the ice begins to break apart. Huge pieces overturn and crash into the sea. Ice floes break apart and drift away in open sea lanes. As the weather grows warmer, more ice breaks away from land, and storms blow it out to sea. Now, it is easier to see where land ends and the ocean begins.

All plants and living creatures seem to be in a hurry during the short arctic spring and summer. Very rapidly, plants grow, flower, and bear fruit. Birds and

A flock of snow geese fills the sky over the arctic tundra of northern Alaska.

animals mate and raise their young. Many creatures shed their winter coats and acquire coats that blend with their summer surroundings. It is a time of plenty and a time of great activity.

On the tundra, the sun gradually comes up earlier and sets later until, by about the middle of May, it no longer sets. It circles the sky twenty-four hours each day. Offshore, thawing snow picks up the sun's

warmth and a little water covers the ice. On land, snow slides down the slopes. Where the warmer temperatures of the tundra meet the colder temperatures of the ocean, fog forms.

The boggy tundra, almost free of snow, has a fresh carpet of grasses and reindeer moss. Now, too, the tundra blossoms with brightly colored plants. Purple saxifrage spread across the valleys. Arctic poppies cover plateaus. Buttercups fill the meadows. Even vegetable crops can be raised under the constant sunshine.

A foot or two below these blooms, the permafrost layer remains frozen. In some places, permafrost reaches down only a few feet. In other places, it reaches more than 1,000 feet (301 meters) beneath the surface.

Animals of the Tundra

Herds of migrating caribou graze along the foothills and paw away snow to reach tasty lichens. Packs of wolves follow, waiting for the chance to separate a single animal from the herd. Wolves will continue to hunt the caribou as long as they remain here.

Musk oxen also graze on the tundra. However,

A caribou with magnificent antlers moves along the foothills of a rugged area in Alaska.

they are not such easy prey for wolves. When threatened, the males form a tight circle around the females and calves, standing shoulder to shoulder, with their heads facing out. With their dark, shaggy coats and sharp horns, the bulls make an impressive, and effective, barrier. Wolves quickly learn to leave the musk oxen alone and look for easier meals.

Meanwhile, other animals are beginning to come out of **hibernation**. Arctic ground squirrels emerge from their burrows. They dig up rootlets to eat, along with sprouts and leaves. These creatures have survived the winter with an average body temperature of just 34°F (1°C) and only a few heartbeats per minute.

Lemmings, too, become restless. Some of them became meals when arctic foxes dug them out of their burrows during the winter months. The surviving lemmings seem to come out all at the same time and dart here and there until they cover the tundra. Owls and hawks snatch them for meals. Soon, their burrows will be flooded by streams of melting snow. Each female lemming has several litters of babies during the spring and summer. The babies have to grow rapidly to be able to live through the arctic winter.

As **pack ice** breaks up, polar bears come to land.

A group of polar bears rests on snow-covered ground in northern Alaska.

Their winter hunting is finished, and now they feed on lemmings or dead seals and whales that have been washed ashore. During the summer months, polar bears often have trouble getting rid of excess heat. They must cool off by lying on the ice or getting into the water.

Arctic foxes also come to land from the pack ice. On the tundra, they feed on birds, eggs, and lemmings.

As the weather grows warmer, their coats change to a brown-gray color that blends with their surroundings. When snow falls, their coats change back again to white. Then only a black nose and yellowish eyes keep them from blending completely with their winter territory.

As summer passes, the sun begins to dip below the **horizon**. Each day it sets a little earlier and rises a little later. Migrating birds must soon be prepared for another long flight. Many young animals must also be strong enough to endure a long journey.

Now, the soil of the tundra begins to glisten with frost. Birds and animals gather in groups and begin their southward migrations. Only a few birds, including the snowy owl, raven, ptarmigan, and gyrfalcon, remain along with a small number of the larger arctic animals.

Again, open water begins to freeze, and the border between land and sea becomes an unbroken stretch of ice and snow. The bitter cold of the arctic winter will soon spread throughout the roof of the world.

# Arctic Explorers

Explorers first reached the North Pole in 1908 or 1909, depending on whose story is correct. Most history books say that Admiral Robert E. Peary led the first expedition to reach the North Pole. Yet some historians believe that Dr. Frederick A. Cook actually arrived there first.

In April 1909, Dr. Cook sent a cablegram. It read: "Reached North Pole April 21, 1908." A few days later, Commander Peary sent a cable: "I have the Pole, April 6, 1909."

Because the Arctic has such harsh weather conditions, and modern communications did not exist in the early 1900s, reporting on an arctic expedition could take a great deal of time. Regardless of which American explorer arrived first, the North Pole was no longer an unknown place at the top of the earth. For years, explorers from many nations had attempted to find a shortcut from Europe to the Orient. Now, the first step had been taken to make this possible.

The Early Expeditions

Both Admiral Peary and Dr. Cook endured many hardships as they crossed the arctic ice. Since they were pioneers in this cold part of the world, they had to learn much by trial and error.

Both explorers took ships as far as possible along the arctic coast of Greenland. Their ships rammed into the ice and forced their way through it. When the ships could go no farther, the crew unloaded the supplies for the trip and reloaded them onto dogsleds.

In order to keep the sleds as light as possible, they took along only supplies that were most needed. Time, too, was important, and there was little to spare for preparing meals. Men of Dr. Cook's expedition stopped once a day to eat. Then, they often ate raw meat, which they also fed to their dogs. Perhaps the dogs that pulled these sleds deserve part of the credit. Without them, neither Admiral Peary nor Dr. Cook could have reached the North Pole.

On smooth ice, these dogs could travel swiftly. But arctic ice is not smooth. The grinding and cracking of large ice floes cause jagged icy ridges and open lanes of water. In these conditions, fifteen to twenty miles (twenty-four to thirty-two kilometers) per day was a

Admiral Robert E. Peary during one of his arctic expeditions. His chief assistant, Matthew Henson, and four native arctic men were part of the team that reached the North Pole.

good traveling speed for a dog team. Even then, when mountains of ice loomed up ahead and the explorers could not go around them, dogs and men worked together to pull the sleds over these barriers.

North of the tree line in the Arctic, there is nothing to break the force of the wind. No clothing can completely protect a person from these icy blasts. At -76°F (-60°C) in calm weather or in -22°F (-30°C) with a twenty-mile-per-hour wind, exposed flesh can freeze in one minute.

In addition to the extreme cold, the glare created by the sun shining on the snow sometimes blinded the explorers. Often they were sunburned.

Sometimes the men slept in hastily constructed shelters. At other times they slept in snowdrifts. On the arctic ice cap, snow covers both old, solid ice and newly formed ice. At any time, day or night, a sled could break through the ice, sending dogs, people, or supplies into the icy water. Considering the dangers and hardships of traveling in the Arctic, these explorers needed great courage to make such a bold journey.

When the Cook and Peary expeditions reached the North Pole, their journey was only half-finished. They still had to return over the same dangerous route.

Flying to the Pole

Now that explorers with dogsleds had reached the North Pole, other explorers began to think of reaching it in other ways. One of these was an American, Admiral Richard E. Byrd.

Flying was still a new and uncertain way to travel when Admiral Byrd planned his trip by plane to the North Pole. He knew he must fly over 1,600 miles (2,576 kilometers) of polar ice. Byrd learned all he could about airplane engines and oil. The instruments in his tri-motored monoplane, *Josephine Ford*, were the best available.

With fifty men, a sturdy ship, and warm clothing, he started his journey. The expedition's ship sailed to northern Greenland, where the crew set up camp. Then, they prepared the plane to go on.

On May 9, 1926, Admiral Byrd's plane, equipped with landing skiis, was ready. Byrd and his mechanic, Floyd Bennett, brought the plane down a runway built from the top of a hill to the water and took off on their flight.

Almost immediately, they had mechanical problems. When oil started to leak from an engine, they feared that a motor could fail. Since there was no place

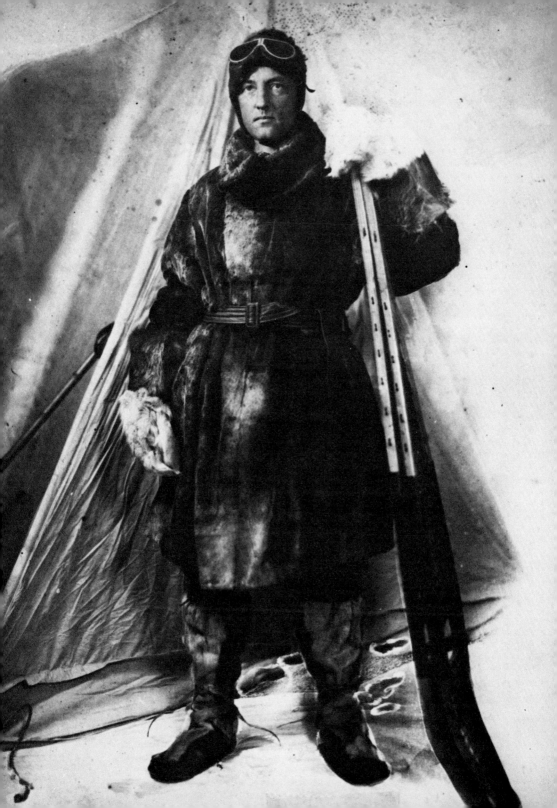

to land, the explorers kept going. Next, Byrd dropped an instrument, and it broke. Now, he had only "**dead reckoning**" to determine their location and flight direction. In spite of the crew's problems, the plane reached the North Pole and returned to its base. Byrd and Bennett had made history!

Meanwhile, a Norwegian explorer was also trying to fly over the North Pole. In 1911, Roald Amundsen had led the first expedition to reach the South Pole. Now, three days after Byrd and Bennett, Amundsen passed over the North Pole in a lighter-than-air airship, the dirigible *Norge*. On this trip he crossed the entire Arctic Ocean from Spitsbergen—a group of islands north of Norway—to a point in northern Alaska in North America.

In less than twenty years, four courageous explorers had reached the North Pole and had gained valuable information about the arctic region. Because of these early explorers, people around the world became interested in the Arctic. In the coming years, expeditions of many kinds reached the North Pole, traveling by plane, submarine, and snowmobile. With the help of airdrops of food and equipment, some explorers have even walked to the Pole.

Admiral Richard E. Byrd flew over 1,600 miles (2,576 kilometers) of polar ice to reach the North Pole.

The Steger Expedition

Will Steger, however, headed an expedition that was more like those of Cook and Peary. Rather than rely on mechanical transportation, Steger decided to journey to the North Pole by dogsled. Members of his handpicked team came from the United States, Canada, and New Zealand, and included a woman, Ann Bancroft. After months of survival training in northern Minnesota, eight people and forty-nine sled dogs were ready. On March 8, 1986, the Steger International Polar Expedition set out across the arctic ice from northern Canada.

Because the seven men and one woman would not receive airdrops of food and equipment, they had to carry enough food for the trip to the Pole, and for all the dogs that were needed to haul the added weight. The heavy sleds could not easily cross the huge ridges of arctic ice. Sometimes the team members could travel no more than a few miles a day. Since they had to go around many of these ice barriers, they could not travel in a straight line. They had to travel nearly twice the distance that an airplane would cover flying a direct route to the Pole.

As the voyage wore on, their loads became lighter,

Members of the Steger expedition pull one of their sleds over a pressure ridge on their way to the North Pole.

Will Steger/Firth Photo Bank

and they found less of a need for the heavy sleds. They simply cut off pieces of sleds and burned them for extra warmth in their tent. The expedition had arranged for airlifts to pick up dogs that were no longer needed.

The journey was hard for everyone on the team. Temperatures reached -70°F (-57°C), and when they weren't out pushing with the dogs, they were huddled inside a small tent with no privacy. The tension and close quarters sometimes caused the team members to quarrel.

Outside, the trip wasn't any easier. Crossing ice ridges and **leads** was backbreaking, and often dangerous, work. At one point as Bancroft prepared to jump over an opening in the ice, the edge of the snow gave way beneath her. She fell into the water up to her waist, but grabbed on to the edge and managed to scramble back onto the ice. Bancroft quickly changed out of her wet clothes before they could freeze on her body. She was unhurt, but she said it took two days to get over her chills.

Other members of the expedition were not as lucky. One had been hit by a bouncing sled and injured several ribs. Another suffered from frostbitten feet.

After falling into the cold arctic waters, Ann Bancroft rushes to change her wet, freezing clothes.

Will Steger/Firth Photo Bank

The two men had to be airlifted out along with some of the dogs.

Even though there were now only six humans and twenty-one dogs to feed, the supplies were running low. Some of the dogs made matters worse by chewing through their restraining rope and eating twenty precious pounds (nine kilograms) of food.

The team pushed on in a race against the approaching spring thaw and the dwindling food supplies. Finally, they were within twenty miles (thirty-two kilometers) of the Pole, and in good spirits. They traveled along at a fast pace and, at midnight, decided to sleep and check their position in the morning.

On the fifty-sixth day of the expedition, the team awakened to their navigator's announcement: "We don't have to travel today. We're here!" The expedition had unknowingly stopped within two hundred yards of the North Pole. They radioed to verify their position and to call for an airlift out. While they waited for the planes to pick them up, the tired team enjoyed the luxury of crawling back into their sleeping bags.

On May 1, 1986, the Steger International Polar Expedition completed the first confirmed dogsled expedition to the North Pole without resupply. Ann Ban-

The Steger International Polar Expedition team members hold up the American flag at the North Pole. They also displayed the Canadian flag, and carried the flags of other nations.

croft became the first woman to reach the North Pole. When reporters came to greet the explorers at the Pole, Bancroft read a declaration that expressed the feelings of the whole team: "As we, six adventurers from different parts of the world, stand where the lines of longitude of all countries meet, we believe this journey stands for hope—hope that other seemingly impossible goals can be met by people everywhere."

The Steger team members were not the first to discover in themselves the courage and determination needed to conquer the arctic. And they will not be the last. Yet through their expedition, they joined a select group of history-making arctic explorers.

Nautilus 90° North

Unlike other arctic expeditions, one history-making mission took place beneath the ice. Surrounded by secrecy, the nuclear-powered submarine, *Nautilus*, left its dock in Seattle. The year was 1957, and its U.S. Navy captain was Commander William Anderson. When the underwater trip was underway, Commander Anderson made an important announcement to his crew. The *Nautilus* would travel under the arctic ice and, if possible, to the North Pole.

A Special Submarine and Crew

Excitement mounted. Each member of this hand-picked, highly skilled, and courageous crew worked well as a team. The crew had been through many deep-water missions together. Yet, this one was unlike any journey they had made before.

The whale-shaped *Nautilus* was 320 feet (98 meters) in length—longer than a football field—and 28 feet (8.5 meters) in diameter. The temperature inside

The Nautilus, *a history-making nuclear submarine, heads out to sea.*

the submarine remained a constant 72°F (22°C). Because the vessel did not have to use space to carry batteries and fuel tanks as non-nuclear submarines did, the crew had comfortable quarters.

The *Nautilus* carried all of the latest equipment of its time. It also had several features that had been added for this journey under the ice cap. A specially designed **gyrocompass** had been installed for use near

the North Pole, where magnetic compasses are not reliable. In addition, the submarine had upward-pointing **sonar**. This device uses sound waves to locate ice underwater in the same way that ordinary sonar shows the ocean bottom. It would show how thick the ice was as the *Nautilus* moved farther and farther north in the Arctic Ocean. The special sonar would also locate the leads, narrow water passages in pack ice, and the **polynias**, large areas of open water enclosed by ice. The crew needed this information so that the submarine could put up its **periscope**. The *Nautilus* needed refueling only once every two years, and carried enough air to supply the crew for two months.

Even with all its advanced equipment, the vessel's crew had no idea what they would find during their trip into the unknown. Submarines had crept under the edge of the arctic ice before, but none had attempted to go anywhere near the North Pole.

A Test Run under the Ice

Commander Anderson tested the *Nautilus* under these extreme weather conditions in a journey under the ice between Greenland and Spitsbergen. For this trip, he had to rely on instruments. First, he tested the

upward-pointing sonar. The information it provided was charted along with measurements of the distance between the bottom of the submarine and the ocean bottom. For the *Nautilus* to have a safe journey under the ice, it had to receive accurate information from the sonar at all times.

All went well until Commander Anderson attempted to bring the submarine up near the surface to check the area with its periscope. The upward-pointing sonar showed that above them there was an opening in the ice. But as the *Nautilus* ascended, a block of ice smashed the periscope.

Quickly, the *Nautilus* descended, and then made its way out of the ice pack and surfaced. Under difficult conditions, welders repaired the damage.

Commander Anderson was ready to try again. The *Nautilus* traveled deep in the water to within 180 miles (290 kilometers) of the North Pole. Its instruments showed that in some places the ice above the submarine was fifty feet (fifteen meters) thick. Suddenly, an electrical failure caused the gyrocompasses to stop functioning. Without them, it would be too risky to try to complete the journey. Again, Commander Anderson ordered the vessel to turn back.

A crew member checks equipment aboard the Nautilus.

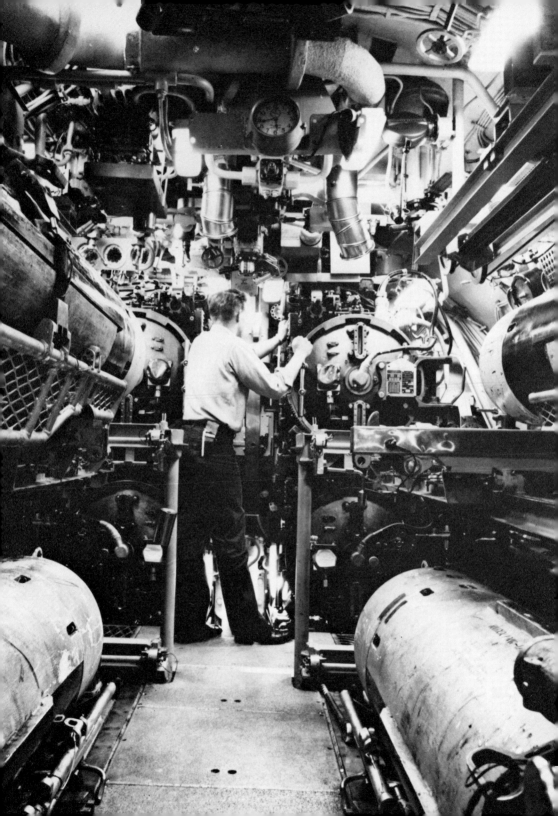

The *Nautilus* reached the safety of the edge of the ice pack. This submarine had gone farther north than any other, but it had not completed its mission. Commander Anderson and the crew wanted the opportunity to try again.

During the next year, Navy workers equipped the *Nautilus* with six new upward-pointing sonar devices. They also installed a closed-circuit television so the crew would be able to look at the underside of the ice.

This time the submarine would attempt to cross the Arctic Ocean from west to east. It crossed the Bering Strait between Alaska and the Soviet Union and moved farther north. Soon the sonar measurements showed that there wasn't much room between the ice above and the ocean floor below. As the *Nautilus* moved farther north, the ice became thicker, but the water did not become deeper. Since the ice above was very irregular, the commander ordered the submarine to slow down and go closer to the ocean floor. This course was risky, but not as risky as hitting a piece of ice overhead. At one spot, the submarine cleared a hanging ridge of ice by only five feet (less than two meters). To the north, the ice would probably become even thicker, and the water shallower.

Commander William Anderson briefs the submarine's crew on ice conditions.

Disappointed, Commander Anderson ordered a course to the south toward open water. Their journey had been started too early in the season.

Nautilus *at the North Pole*

In July 1958, the *Nautilus* made a third attempt at this mission. The submarine submerged beyond Point Barrow, in Alaska, and headed north toward the Pole.

Above the vessel, the ice was still jagged on the underside, but was much thinner than before. The *Nautilus* moved closer and closer to its goal.

Excitement mounted as the crew realized that they would soon reach the North Pole. Commander Anderson stood by in the control room. Finally, he spoke through the intercom: "Stand by. Ten...eight...six... four, three, two, one, mark! August 3, 1958....For the United States and the United States Navy, the North Pole!"

The *Nautilus* had found a passage for nuclear submarines from the Pacific Ocean to the Atlantic Ocean. Its instruments had made an accurate picture of the Arctic Ocean floor and had gathered much valuable new scientific information. Above all, the daring journey had proved that a submarine could travel to the northernmost point on earth.

Their mission accomplished, Commander Anderson set a course to the south. When the *Nautilus* reached a place where it could surface, several hundred miles from the Pole, the submarine's antenna was extended. A radio operator tapped out the message that announced their arrival at the North Pole to the world: *Nautilus* 90° north!

6 Survival in the Arctic

The northern parts of Europe, Asia, and North America extend into the Arctic Ocean. On these continents, a few people pushed northward into the Arctic thousands of years ago. They brought many customs with them from their communities to the south, and adapted their way of life to the arctic region. Today, these people are known around the world as Eskimos. Most arctic people of North America and Greenland call themselves Inuit, which means "human beings." In the far north of Europe and Asia, people call themselves by other names.

Each arctic family or community lived in the way in which the people had the best chance for survival. Families divided the work. Often, men were hunters and trappers, while women prepared and sewed skins and raised dogs. Children helped with chores such as bringing in ice for drinking water. Grandparents and aunts and uncles usually lived with the parents and children.

No matter where they lived, people of the Arctic had much in common. Their greatest enemy was the harsh climate. They survived by adapting to their environment, or surroundings, in every way possible, and by using every available resource. When the people hunted polar bears and seals, they ate the flesh and used the **blubber**, or fat, for fuel. They stretched and dried the animal skins and made them into clothing or tents. Animal bones became human tools.

Arctic Clothes and Houses

Arctic people learned from experience which skins were best suited for clothing. Two layers of caribou skin back to back provided warm winter clothing. Parkas were made so that the people could pull their arms inside for extra warmth. And, if someone fell in the water, they became life preservers. Waterproof sealskin, often padded with fur, made excellent shoe soles. These items of clothing lasted a year, and then had to be replaced.

Arctic people built houses from local materials that suited their needs. Central Canadians, who were nomads, lived in houses made from snow and ice. These igloos worked well for conserving heat, because

This native Alaskan family dresses in both traditional and modern clothes, and travels by dogsled.

their low entrances and domed shape trapped warm air and kept it inside.

Some arctic people, including North Alaskans, built sod houses that were partly underground. They dug a pit, put a support made of driftwood or whalebone across the top, and covered it with sod cut from the tundra and dried. Often, several families shared these earth-sheltered homes.

Nenets, who hunted whales in both the Barents and Kara seas, often lived in tents. The inhabitants of West Greenland made houses of stone and turf.

Arctic Transportation

Transportation in the Arctic varied according to the season. The **umiak**, a kind of boat, often provided water transportation. Its frame was made of driftwood lashed together with sealskin thongs. Stretched seal or walrus hides covered the frame. As a flat-bottomed, lightweight, durable craft, the umiak was well suited to arctic waters. It could survive shocks that would shatter boats made from other materials. More than twenty men could paddle one umiak as they hunted whales.

Some people hunted in **kayaks**, swift little boats

Umiaks like this one are still used by native people in the Arctic.

which were also covered with seal or walrus hides. Hunters lashed their waterproof seal-intestine shirts to their kayaks to keep dry in case of spills.

When arctic people traveled on the snow, many used dogsleds. It took a number of dogs to pull one sled. Certain dogs, such as Alaskan huskies, could survive the harsh climate and could pull the sleds well. Hunters could feed their huskies blubber—the same kind of food they often ate.

Food—a Constant Struggle

Food was a constant problem for everyone who lived in arctic regions. If hunters killed a whale, several families could live all winter from its flesh and blubber. Refrigeration was not a problem. They simply buried the meat in a snowdrift. Whale bones made hunting bows and drying racks for skins.

Most arctic people who lived along the coast hunted seals and walruses for food. They used these animals' skins for clothes, boats, and summer tents. They used the animal fat as oil for lamps to light and heat their homes. **Tendons** of the animals became thread for sewing.

The Lapps lived near the Norwegian Sea where

they received warmth from the Gulf Stream. Because the climate was not as harsh in this area, they were one of the few arctic peoples who were able to do some farming in addition to fishing and whaling.

Reindeer, which are closely related to caribou, were an important resource for many arctic people. Some hunted reindeer by following the migrations of wild herds. Others, like the Lapps, kept herds of reindeer and milked them. In some places they were taught to pull sleds and carry loads. People also rode them. The Evenks, who lived in Siberia near the Yakuts, rode their reindeer high on the shoulders so they would not injure the animals' weak backs.

In the Arctic, people often had to work hard to get water as well as food. Because of the extremely dry air, they needed to drink large amounts of water to replace the water vapor lost in breathing the cold, dry air. Usually, the people had to chop and melt ice to get drinking water. Sometimes, hunters filled the stomach of a freshly killed caribou with snow. The animal's body heat would melt the snow, providing the hunters with water.

Even with all of their **adaptations** to the conditions of the Arctic, life was often a struggle. An unusually

long and severe winter could cause many people to go
hungry or even to starve. Parents taught their children
what they needed to know to survive—how to hunt,
how to keep from freezing in cold weather, how to
make animal skins into clothing, and how to waterproof them.

Perhaps the mid-winter darkness was the hardest
time of the arctic year. If people had enough food to last
through the cold, dark months, they would stay home
with their families and visit relatives and friends in
the community. Some people used this time to make
carvings of animals or humans from ivory or bone.
They carved tools such as knives for scraping animal
skins, and harpoons for hunting seals. These carvings
and tools help us understand what life in the Arctic
was like long ago.

As transportation and communication improved,
the world learned more and more about the people who
lived at the roof of the world. For those who lived in the
far north, modern ways of life brought many changes.

*Using a handmade drill "powered" by a bow and leather thong device, a
native Alaskan carves elegant figures from chunks of bare ivory.*

The Modern Arctic

During World War II, modern technology came suddenly to the Arctic when air bases were built in some places. Ships and planes brought in equipment and people. Military towns sprang up, bringing thousands of people from the south to areas where just a few hundred arctic people had lived before. After the war, the U.S. and Soviet governments built fighter bases and early warning radar systems in the far north to defend against an attack from the other side of the Pole.

A Changing Way of Life

These new residents bought or traded for many things the arctic people had—from walrus tusks to clothing made from animal skins. At first, the northern people did not understand why these newcomers were so fascinated with items that seemed ordinary to them. Soon, though, the natives offered to sell or trade their belongings. They also became interested in items the

people from the south had brought along. Many of these new gadgets, they found, made their way of life easier.

Another big change came about in Alaska. After oil was discovered in the 1960s and 1970s, construction of the Alaskan pipeline began so that the oil could be transported to the south. Almost overnight, heavy equipment and oil workers moved into the areas where the pipeline would be built.

The oil companies needed workers and hired Alaskans at good salaries. Some Alaskan men decided to work on the pipeline for a paycheck and to hunt in the traditional way during their time off. Now, these workers had money to buy all kinds of food, clothing, machines, and household goods. Young people, particularly, were interested in these changes. They were fascinated with snowmobiles and with new kinds of food and clothing. Suddenly, to some of them, the old ways of life did not seem very attractive. They wanted to try all of the new products.

Such rapid changes caused problems in families. Often, parents and grandparents wanted children to follow the traditional ways of life and learn to hunt and fish as their parents and grandparents had. Some-

times, though, the young people in a family decided to try the new ways. They went to schools far away. When they returned, they found that the old ways no longer had meaning for them. Often, there was no place in the Arctic to use what they had learned.

Others decided to continue their traditional ways of life. Yet, even for them, modern technology affected their lives. Because snowmobiles moved faster than dogsleds, some native people acquired snowmobiles. And since rifles made hunting easier, many bought or traded for rifles.

A Blending of Old and New

The old and the new ways were blending. To many people, killing whales seemed less important when they could buy a variety of meats, fruits, and vegetables at a nearby store. Gradually, towns in the Arctic came to have the same kinds of stores as those found throughout the United States. Still, even with all these changes, some of the old ways remain.

Whaling in the Arctic has not changed as much as other types of hunting. Once a whale is killed, many people work together. After pulling it out of the water, they pull away the thick blubber with hooks and di-

Workers build a section of the Alaska pipeline in a mountainous region of the northernmost U.S. state.

Armed with a modern rifle, this native Alaskan hunter waits patiently for a seal to appear. His boat is a traditional one covered by sealskin.

vide the meat in the traditional ways. Then they haul away a slab of blubber, often on a snowmobile. Today, as in the past, the blubber is used for fuel, cooking, and bait for arctic fox traps. As soon as the red meat of this whale is divided, it is taken away and stored in caches dug out of permafrost.

Some Alaskans resent the people from the "south" who have come to their communities in search of new

Native people work together to divide a whale in traditional ways.

sources of natural wealth. They believe this land belongs to the people who have lived here for a long time. Others are pleased by the modern ways. They like the changes in education, medical care, transportation, and communications. And yet, when a job is completed and the company they worked for leaves, they no longer have a paycheck. It is difficult to return to hunting and fishing and go without the money to buy the modern things they have learned to enjoy.

Whether they follow mainly the old or the new ways of life, arctic people must live in two worlds. People from other places will continue to come to the Arctic because governments and industries need new energy sources and are finding them in the far north. As a result, the traditional ways of life will continue to change.

In northern Norway, among the Lapps, less than one person out of ten now follows the reindeer migrations. Many who still herd reindeer use snowmobiles for herding. Since Lapp children go to Norwegian schools, which are often far away, they must live near the school and come home only for visits. In school, the children study the subjects related to modern Norway. At home, they learn how to herd reindeer.

Sometimes these different ways seem far apart. Traditional Lapp parents are upset because their children are not learning more about their heritage. Many young people have left the herds and have become doctors, miners, builders, and teachers. These Lapps have modern homes, automobiles, radios, and television sets.

The 800,000 native people of the Arctic want to have more control over the use of their land and coastal waters. Since they believe it is their right to kill whales for food, they have protested against whaling rules that make it illegal for them to hunt whales. The inhabitants of the far north want to share equally in the development of their homelands. They are meeting with arctic people from other countries to discuss their mutual problems. In some communities, their own candidates have won elections. For everyone, it is a time of great change at the roof of the world.

The Floor of the World

Just as the Arctic is the roof of the world, Antarctica is the floor. At the South Pole, magnetic compasses spin wildly. Here, the only direction is north.

Seasons in Antarctica are reversed from those of the Arctic. Spring and summer are October through March, and fall and winter are April through September. Like the North Pole, the South Pole has six months of light and six months of darkness.

Antarctica, too, has strange, beautiful lights during its winter months. Here, these southern lights are called the **aurora australis**.

The Coldest Place on Earth

Although the Arctic is known for its extremely low temperatures, Antarctica is the coldest place on earth. This southernmost continent, surrounded by water, is twice the size of the United States. It is shaped somewhat like a circular hump with a narrow point extending to the north—the jagged Antarctic

This map of Antarctica shows the region with the South Pole at its center.

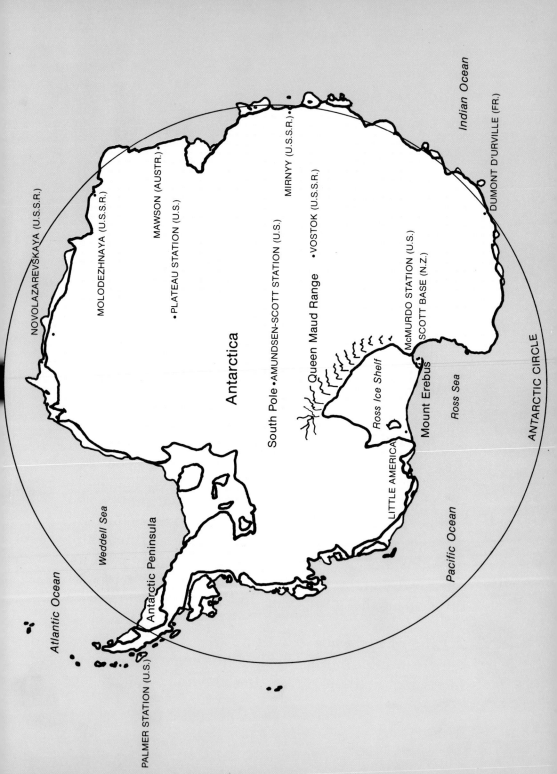

Indian Ocean

DUMONT D'URVILLE (FR.)

MIRNYY (U.S.S.R.)

• VOSTOK (U.S.S.R.)

MAWSON (AUSTR.) •

• PLATEAU STATION (U.S.)

MOLODEZHNAYA (U.S.S.R.)

McMURDO STATION (U.S.)

SCOTT BASE (N.Z.)

NOVOLAZAREVSKAYA (U.S.S.R.)

AMUNDSEN-SCOTT STATION (U.S.)

South Pole •

Antarctica

Queen Maud Range

Ross Ice Shelf

Mount Erebus

Ross Sea

ANTARCTIC CIRCLE

LITTLE AMERICA

Weddell Sea

Antarctic Peninsula

Pacific Ocean

Atlantic Ocean

PALMER STATION (U.S.)

Peninsula, also known as the Palmer Peninsula and as Graham Land. Antarctica has ranges of high mountains and ice plateaus. From its mountain passes, rivers of ice spill into the ocean. The Queen Maud Range divides the continent. One mountain, Mount Erebus, is an active volcano. When it erupts, black ash and fiery lava cover the surrounding ice and snow.

Two seas, the Ross and the Weddell, border Antarctica's northern edge. Each has an ice shelf. The Ross ice barrier is 400 miles (644 kilometers) long, and its jagged cliffs reach 150 feet (46 meters) above the water. Though these two seas pose dangers for ships, they still are the best ocean entrances to the continent at the bottom of the world.

Unlike the Arctic, no warm ocean currents reach Antarctica to temper the climate. And unlike the Arctic Ocean waters, which absorb and give off warmth, the antarctic land mass does not have a similar warming effect. In fact, this region has the coldest temperatures on earth—more than -100°F (-73°C) below zero!

A Land of Extremes

Antarctica has been called "the home of the wind." In its mountainous areas, the howling winds some-

High mountains rise from the ice cap that covers much of Antarctica.

times reach 200 miles (322 kilometers) per hour. They sweep across this continent and whip the seas into huge waves.

Because Antarctica is so cold, it has no rain—**precipitation** comes in the form of snow. The continent receives about four inches (ten centimeters) of moisture each year, which means that it is as dry as a desert. Yet this snow has slowly built up to form the biggest ice cap in the world.

Surrounding Antarctica, the ocean waters remain frozen during the winter months, as in the Arctic. During the antarctic summer, the ice gradually breaks up as it thaws. Waters around Antarctica contain icebergs that have broken off the edges of glaciers as they move slowly downward along mountainsides or valleys and reach the ocean. An iceberg the size of Massachusetts has been seen near the Ross Ice Shelf.

Antarctica has no trees. Some mosses and hardy, slow-growing lichens have adapted to the extreme conditions on parts of this cold continent. Sometimes they grow inside porous rocks of dry antarctic valleys.

Despite its stormy seas, ice cliffs, and ragged, windswept mountains, the Antarctic is a land of great natural beauty. On a sunny day, the blue sea, the

Huge icebergs such as this one break off from the edges of antarctic glaciers.

sparkling white ice and snow, and the clean, fresh air make the extreme cold seem less of a burden to the people who travel there. Fascinating animals—penguins, seals, and whales—thrive in this faraway region. Far more than people, they have adapted to the conditions at the floor of the world.

The Creatures of Antarctica

Antarctica has no large land animals, but penguins, seals, whales, and sea birds live in and above its surrounding waters. Adélie penguins feed on **krill**, small shrimplike creatures, at the surface of the cold antarctic seas. Once in a while, they swim deeper to eat fish and squid.

Antarctic Penguins

The Adélie penguin's streamlined body is well suited to ocean life. In the water, its flipperlike wings serve as paddles. While most birds' bones are hollow, penguins' bones are solid, which gives them added weight for diving. Oily feathers provide the birds with watertight coats. Violent antarctic storms and ocean waves do not bother this creature as it swims in its natural home among icebergs and ice floes. If the water at the surface becomes too rough, it moves to calmer water below the surface.

Though a penguin seldom gets cold in Antarctica,

These Adélie penguins nest in a large colony on the coast of Antarctica.

it sometimes becomes too hot. Then, it must fluff out its coat to allow some of the heat to escape. In that way it controls its body temperature.

When a penguin nears the shore, it swims underwater, and then pops onto land like a jack-in-the-box. While penguins are at home in the ocean, on land these creatures stand upright and waddle along awkwardly, or slide on their bellies. To people, they may seem like little clowns.

Penguins must go to land to nest. In October, springtime in Antarctica, Adélie penguins land on the bare rocks where they were hatched. Here, they will nest in large **rookeries**, or colonies, each pair of penguins in the same nest as the year before. Imagine trying to locate a certain nest among thousands, crowded closely together, that look very much alike. Once the nest is found, the male penguin has to repair it. It must be scooped out and the sides built up with stones, replacing those that are missing. The male may have to go a great distance to find suitable building stones. While building, he must also keep other penguins from stealing his stones.

When the nest is completed, the female lays two bluish white eggs. The male keeps the eggs warm and

guards the nest from **predators** while the female feeds in the ocean for a week or more. To keep the eggs at a constant temperature, the male sits on the nest with the eggs balanced on top of his feet and pressed into his warm body.

When the chicks hatch, they are covered with a feathery down coat. Now, the parents take turns guarding them and waddling to the ocean to get food. After several weeks, because of the chicks' increased appetite, both parents must hunt for food.

With both parents gone, penguin babies face a number of dangers. Blizzards sometimes kill them. Antarctic skuas—hawklike gulls—often swoop down on the rookeries and grab an unprotected chick. Within two months, the remaining penguin babies shed their down, grow adult feathers, and begin swimming in their natural ocean home.

The four-foot (more than one-meter) long Emperor penguin also lives in Antarctica. This large bird may weigh up to eighty pounds (thirty-six kilograms). It raises its young during the coldest part of the year— without building a nest!

The female Emperor penguin lays one green egg. Then the male protects the egg while the female wad-

Emperor penguins raise their young during the coldest part of the antarctic year.

dles to the ocean to feed. If left exposed, the egg would freeze in about one minute.

The male balances the egg on his feet, wraps a fold of skin around it, and stands for two months waiting for it to hatch. To keep themselves and the eggs warmer, many penguins huddle together. During this time, temperatures may drop to -70°F (-57°C), and the birds may have to withstand hurricane-force bliz-

zards. Male Emperor penguins do not eat during these two months. About the time the chick hatches, the mother returns with food and takes over nursery duties while the father goes to the ocean to feed.

Seals and Whales

Several kinds of seals also live in the Antarctic. The Weddell seal is the world's southernmost **mammal**. It reaches ten feet (three meters) in length and 1,000 pounds (454 kilograms) in weight. This seal has a remarkable ability to live on and under the antarctic ice. It feeds underwater and can remain there for forty-five minutes before it must return to the surface to breathe. It keeps breathing holes open by using them constantly and by sawing them open with its front teeth when the holes begin to freeze over.

The Weddell seal has an unusual **metabolism**. Its body burns fuel at more than twice the rate of land animals. Also, a layer of blubber provides excellent protection from the cold. If temperatures become too cold at the water's surface, these seals dive to reach warmer water below. Sometimes they even take naps underwater.

Weddell seal pups are born with fluffy tan fur. If a

A Weddell seal rests on the ice near Scott Base, New Zealand's research station in Antarctica.

pup's coat gets wet, the moisture freezes almost immediately and falls off in ice crystals. That way the
pup stays dry. In a warmer area, where the moisture
does not freeze so rapidly, the pup might easily become chilled and die.

Of all the antarctic seals, the leopard seal is the
most feared predator. This twelve-foot (3.7-meter)
long hunter lurks under ice shelves waiting for pen-

guins to swim by. With a sudden burst of speed, it grabs the smaller animal in the water or on the edge of the ice. If a penguin is not available, it may kill another seal. A leopard seal can travel faster on rough ice than a man can run.

Several kinds of whales, including the fin, blue, humpback, and southern right, swim in antarctic waters. The killer whale, which is more closely related to dolphins than whales, also hunts penguins. This creature moves through the ocean near the edge of the ice. While it will chase penguins beneath the water's surface, often the penguins escape by leaping out of the water onto the ice. Of all the creatures of Antarctica, the penguin may be the best adapted to survive in this cold and dangerous environment.

Explorers and Research Stations

In centuries past, a number of explorers set out in search of an unknown "southern land." In 1768, Captain James Cook of England sailed farther south than anyone had sailed before, but did not reach it. Half a century later, a young American, Nathaniel Palmer, sailed his small seal-hunting ship to the long, narrow peninsula that forms the northern part of Antarctica. Twenty years later, an American naval officer, Lieutenant Charles Wilkes, discovered the main part of the continent. The following year, Sir James Clark Ross, heading a British expedition, sailed as far south as the Ross Sea. Then, for nearly a century, the world seemed to lose interest in Antarctica.

In 1911, the Norwegian explorer, Roald Amundsen, decided to try to reach the South Pole. Amundsen planned with great care for a journey by dogsled across the vast, rugged continent. His team members built snow beacons every three miles (five kilometers) to help the expedition find its way back. Every sixty

miles (ninety-seven kilometers), they stored food and other supplies. In an orderly way, but with many hardships, Roald Amundsen and his dogsleds reached the South Pole on December 16, 1911.

Admiral Byrd in Antarctica

After flying to the North Pole in 1926, Admiral Richard E. Byrd organized a larger expedition to explore and study Antarctica and reach the South Pole. In December 1928, two ships, the *City of New York*, and the *Eleanor Bolling*, pulled away from a New Zealand dock. A steel towing rope fastened the two ships together. They sailed toward Antarctica early in the summer, the only time of the year they could get through these iceberg-filled waters. Along the way, these ships were scheduled to meet the Norwegian whaler, *Larsen*, whose captain had volunteered to tow the *City of New York* through the ice pack.

With Admiral Byrd on this expedition were scientific experts in various fields. In all, fifty-three men and 100 sled dogs set out for the southernmost continent.

Admiral Byrd searched for the *Larsen* as huge masses of ice forced the ships to change their course

Roald Amundsen, a famous Norwegian explorer, led the first expedition to reach the South Pole. Amundsen devoted much of his life to polar exploration.

again and again. Time was running out, Finally, they spotted the Norwegian whaler!

Now, the *Bolling* returned to New Zealand for another load of supplies. The *Larsen* towed the *City of New York* through the ice, pushing, pulling, and widening the way. The ice tested the *City of New York's* ability to withstand its crushing pressure and violent crashes against the ship's timbers. After ten days, they arrived at the open water of the Ross Sea.

When the whaler left, the *City of New York* was on its own. Ahead lay the Ross Ice Shelf. Admiral Byrd had to find a way through this barrier, and locate a place where tons of supplies could be landed—enough to furnish the expedition's members with everything they would need for the winter.

When Byrd found the right place, unloading began at a feverish pace. Nine miles inland, the expedition planned to build a small antarctic town which they had decided to call "Little America." Everybody helped unload supplies, and the dogs pulled load after load to the site where Little America would be built. When the dogs could not pull the loads, men roped themselves to the teams and helped pull. Among the supplies were three airplanes—a single-engine Fairchild, a larger

single-engine Fokker, and a huge Ford tri-motor. Byrd planned to use them to help explore the continent. As soon as possible, he made several flights to photograph and map the surrounding region.

In a race against the approaching antarctic winter, the men began to build Little America. They dug foundations in the ice deep enough so that less than half of each building extended above the surface of the ice. Along with their living quarters, they erected radio towers and storehouses.

The *Bolling* returned with another load of supplies. Then, just in time, both ships sailed back to New Zealand for the winter. Soon after they left, ice began to form on the water's surface.

At Little America, the hard work continued. Men hollowed tunnels out of the ice to connect the buildings. They buried the biggest airplane, the *Floyd Bennett*, in a huge hole dug in the ice. At last the expedition was ready for the icy blasts of the antarctic winter.

Late in April, the sun vanished for the winter. Blizzards roared down upon Little America. Temperatures dropped far below zero. In the extreme cold, steel turned brittle, and kerosene became thick.

During the winter, housekeeping chores still had

The Floyd Bennett *in Antarctica before its history-making flight.*

to be done. One of the most difficult jobs was melting enough snow to supply water for the entire "town." Expedition members also gathered scientific data about this icy land. They recorded temperatures, **barometric** and **humidity readings**, and wind speeds.

Meanwhile, Admiral Byrd planned two more expeditions. By October, spring in Antarctica , all was ready. A scientific team, headed by Dr. Lawrence

Gould, started a **geological** exploration of the land masses of Antarctica. As the team's members traveled by dogsled, they dropped off emergency supplies and marked the trail with orange flags on bamboo poles.

Admiral Byrd and his crew prepared to fly to the South Pole in the big Ford tri-motor. Their plane was equipped with skiis that were wider and longer than those ordinarily used on planes. If they had engine trouble and had to land, they could be lost forever in the antarctic wilderness.

Finally, the perfect day came for Admiral Byrd's flight. Five hours after takeoff, the plane's crew saw Dr. Gould's geological party camped at the base of the Queen Maud Range. After dropping a parachute with a few supplies, they were off to the unknown.

Among the mountain peaks, the **altimeter** showed an altitude of 9,600 feet (2,928 meters) above sea level. Now, the *Floyd Bennett* would fly no higher with the weight they carried in the plane. The crew lessened the load by throwing one bag of food overboard. The plane gained some altitude, but not enough to clear the mountains that loomed ahead of them. The crew threw out another and another and still another bag—enough food to last four men for a month.

An artist's view of Admiral Byrd's flight to the South Pole.

With less weight to carry, the *Floyd Bennett* gained enough altitude to fly over the high mountains. Admiral Byrd checked the plane's position again and again. Finally, they reached the South Pole. On that day, November 29, 1929, Admiral Byrd dropped an American flag weighted with a stone as the plane passed over the Pole. Immediately, they turned and flew back toward Little America.

Both expeditions planned by Byrd had been successfully completed during the short spring and summer. Antarctic ground surveys had been made, and the Pole had been reached. Much scientific data had been gathered concerning weather and winds.

The men began to take apart Little America. When the *City of New York* arrived through the ice pack, they were ready to load the ship and start home.

This expedition set the stage for three more expeditions led by Admiral Byrd in the coming years. Each one added to our knowledge of Antarctica. Byrd's daring explorations helped make it possible for research stations to be set up in Antarctica.

International Research Stations

The modern exploration of Antarctica began in 1957 during the International Geophysical Year. Sixty-six nations took part in this event, and twelve nations, including the United States, set up bases in Antarctica. Each base, or station, works independently, but the knowledge gained by its scientists is shared with all of the others. Most scientists do research here only during the antarctic summer months. Some stay throughout the year.

McMurdo Station, known as MacTown, is by far the largest. Here, during the summer, live 800 to 1,200 people—scientists, U.S. Navy personnel, helicopter mechanics, truck drivers, and men and women who keep the town running. They sleep in dormitories and eat in a big mess hall. MacTown has a plant which makes fresh water from seawater, laboratories, a weather station, workshops, an administration building, garages, a chapel, and a gym. Roads link the buildings, and water pipes covered by insulated tin tubes run above ground from building to building. Water is a precious resource. MacTown's residents are allowed two-minute showers twice a week.

Just outside the town is a helicopter pad. Helicopters are an important method of transporation here.

Willie Field, located five miles from town, is the permanent airport for the McMurdo Ice Shelf. It is also a small town with a population of 100 people. Weather reports are transmitted from the field to aircraft every hour. If a special report comes, it usually means bad news about the weather.

On Thanksgiving, MacTown celebrates with a parade. Decorated tractors serve as the floats. The parade is followed by the Penguin Bowl—a football

game between the U.S. Navy personnel and civilians of MacTown.

A great deal of research is done at McMurdo Station. Many scientists from McMurdo travel to other field camps, where they live in special tents and collect data for their research projects. **Glaciologists** study the antarctic ice sheet. **Geologists** at this station study Mount Erebus, Antarctica's only active volcano.

Scientists from different fields also share data for common research projects. Because there is very little pollution in the atmosphere over Antarctica, scientists find it is an ideal place to study atmospheric conditions. Researchers are especially interested in the **greenhouse effect**. According to this theory, pollutants trap heat energy in the atmosphere and cause a general warming trend in the earth's climate. Small temperature changes in this cold continent could cause some melting of the ice cap. If large areas of ice melted, the water could raise the ocean level and cause flooding in other parts of the world.

The **ozone hole** is another major research project. The **ozone layer** in the atmosphere screens out much ultraviolet light that is harmful to life on earth. Fluorocarbons, which are used in aerosol sprays, float up to

the ozone layer where ultraviolet rays from the sun break them up and release chlorine **atoms**. The chlorine atoms react with other chemicals in the atmosphere and reduce the concentration of ozone **molecules**, allowing more ultraviolet rays to break through the ozone layer. Between August and October, an "ozone hole"—an area where the ozone layer is very thin—appears in the atmosphere over Antarctica. Although scientists do not know why this "hole" exists, they are using satellites and computerized instruments to get answers. Because the ozone layer is vital to the survival of life on this planet, scientists from many different countries work together to study the changing relationship between humans and the atmosphere.

Two miles from McMurdo is Scott Base, New Zealand's station. Buildings here are connected by sheltered corridors and fire doors. New Zealand scientists conduct research projects at Scott Base, just as scientists from other nations' antarctic stations. The results of such research are shared among all the scientists.

Palmer Station stands on an island just off the Antarctic Peninsula. It lies outside the Antarctic Circle, well north of McMurdo and Scott stations. Here,

A member of a U.S. Navy polar research team uses a drill to test the thickness of an ice floe.

moss grows in deep mounds. Seals nap on the rocky shores, and the sky is full of petrels and skuas. Scientists come to Palmer to carry out research on plant growth, seals, birds, and weather conditions.

Far to the south of Palmer, Scott, and McMurdo stations lies one of the coldest places in Antarctica. Before getting out of the airplane here, visitors must put on a garment that looks like a space suit. Because of the extreme cold, the airplane's engines are not shut down during passenger and cargo unloading or refueling. Visitors must walk slowly so that they will not become dizzy and disoriented at the 9,300-foot (2,837-meter) altitude.

The flags of the nations that maintain antarctic research stations wave noisily in this windy, cold, white land. At the station is a little barber pole with a mirrored globe on top. A sign at the door welcomes visitors to the South Pole Station, also called Amundsen-Scott Station. Living in two-level buildings under an aluminum protective dome, sixteen men and three women stay here for a year at a time. Six of the nineteen are scientists, and each resident has a private room. The South Pole Station has a library, lounge, billiards, showers, modern toilets, and a shop. The

A tunnel connects buildings at the Amundsen-Scott South Pole Station.

food is excellent, which helps during the nine months of the long antarctic winter. Everyone works hard—often seventy hours a week and 365 days a year—and by year's end, they have become a close-knit group.

The South Pole Station is an excellent place to conduct research. Scientists measure ice thickness, **solar radiation**, and the earth's magnetic forces. They also study the way ice surfaces react to traces of gases

in the atmosphere. From this station, instruments test the purity of air all over the globe. Other instruments track the movements in the earth caused by earthquakes. Beginning with Admiral Byrd's 1928 expedition, and continuing with today's research stations, our knowledge of Antarctica has greatly increased.

Krill, Ice, and Oil

In Antarctica today, airplanes and helicopters transport passengers to the continent from distant airports, or from one antarctic station to another. Icebreaker ships escort cargo ships. Tractors haul supplies across the ice from ships and airfields. Modern, well-equipped research vessels aid scientists.

The Mission of the Hero

The National Science Foundation's research vessel, *Hero*, was built in 1968. For sixteen years it moved busily through the open waters around Antarctica each summer. It glided among icebergs and sometimes slipped within sixty feet (nineteen meters) of leaning ice cliffs, allowing scientists to conduct close-up research. *Hero* was a 760-horsepower **motor sailer**, made of white oak and reinforced at the bow with steel. It was 125 feet (thirty-eight meters) long and had a round bottom which helped it pop up out of the ice. From *Hero*'s deck, scientists studied krill and counted their

For sixteen years the Hero allowed scientists to conduct close-up research along the shores and among the icebergs of Antarctica.

eggs. They dived, wearing special dry suits sealed at the neck, to photograph whales.

In 1984, just before the *Hero* was taken out of service, it performed an important rescue mission. An Argentine station, Almirante Brown Base, burned to the ground, leaving seven winter residents stranded in an emergency hut. All other summer ships had left the area. When the *Hero* arrived, seven men, wearing

orange survival suits, took one last look at the charred ruins of their winter home, and came aboard. For them, it was a sad sight but a welcome rescue—the last important mission of the *Hero*.

Krill—an Important Resource

Today, scientists are studying krill in the seas around Antarctica, continuing the work they had done aboard the *Hero*. Krill is one of this continent's most important and valuable natural resources. These thumb-length, reddish shrimplike animals are the main food of **baleen whales** and of many other antarctic sea creatures.

Schools of krill circle the continent in areas where warmer ocean water collides with icy antarctic currents. The difference in water temperatures stirs up the ocean and brings to the surface great amounts of **nutrients** from the ocean floor. **Phytoplankton** thrive on these nutrients, and krill feed on the phytoplankton. In this way, krill form a key link in the ocean **food chain**.

A school, or group, of krill may contain tens of thousands of these creatures in a cubic meter of ocean water. Sometimes these schools swim at the water's

surface. At other times they swim as far as 600 feet (183 meters) below the surface. Baleen whales cruise through these schools, taking in huge mouthfuls of seawater and krill. These whales then snap their jaws shut and force out the water through their closely spaced **baleen plates**. The krill remains in their mouths, trapped behind the baleen.

Ships from several countries now fish for krill in antarctic waters. The Soviet Union operates 100 giant **trawlers** here. Crews in these vessels bring eight to twelve tons of krill to the surface in one net. They are dried and ground into meal, which is used as food for poultry, farm animals, and farmed fish.

Some scientists believe that krill could be used to help fight world hunger. Krill are the oceans' largest single source of protein, and are rich in vitamins. Hungry people need protein and vitamins. When eaten fresh, krill have very little taste. When frozen or dried, however, they have a strong, unpleasant flavor. **Nutritionists** are looking for ways to improve the taste of frozen or dried krill. Experts say the amount of krill that could be taken from antarctic waters each year would be greater than that of all other kinds of marine life from all the world's oceans.

A Wealth of Fresh Water and Minerals

Ice is another resource of Antarctica. More than two-thirds of the world's fresh water remains frozen in its ice cap. Since some areas of the world lack fresh water for growing crops, watering livestock, and even for drinking, scientists are studying ways to move this frozen fresh water to other places where it is needed. One form in which antarctic ice could be transported is that of an iceberg.

Some scientists think that an iceberg could be towed from Antarctica to southern Australia in two to three months. They estimate that when the iceberg reached Australia, about half of it would be left. This remaining part could be used to supply fresh water and to generate electricity.

Geologists say that Antarctica may have the world's largest coal field. They have also found evidence of valuable deposits of natural gas, iron, copper, gold, and platinum.

The greatest resource of all may be the oil under Antarctica's ice. Geologists have estimated that billions of barrels lie under the ice-covered Weddell and Ross seas. So far, the costs of drilling and transporting antarctic oil are too great to be worth the effort. In

Two scientists climb toward a large snow cliff near Halley Bay in Antarctica.

the future, improved oil-drilling methods and higher oil prices may make this oil more attractive than it is today. Scientists say that offshore oil exploration will not be worth the cost for at least twenty-five years.

Questions about the Future

If much coal, oil, and other minerals are taken from Antarctica, how will such actions affect an environ-

ment so fragile that a scar left by a footprint on moss takes ten years to heal? And if large amounts of krill are taken from antarctic waters, will enough remain to feed whales and other antarctic creatures? For the past thirty years, scientists have carried out research that may help government officials protect the world's only unspoiled continent.

In 1959, because of worldwide concern over the use of Antarctica, the Antarctic Treaty was signed by twelve nations—Argentina, Australia, Belgium, Chile, France, Japan, New Zealand, Norway, South Africa, the Soviet Union, the United Kingdom, and the United States. Since then, six other nations have become parties to the treaty, which took effect in 1961. It promotes scientific study and the sharing of information, and bans military activity on the continent. In 1991, when the treaty comes up for review, the participating countries may open certain areas to oil and mineral exploration.

During the 1980s, the Antarctic Treaty nations have attempted to reach agreement on how to control the use of Antarctica's natural resources. The 1980 Convention for the Conservation of Antarctic Marine Living Resources, known as CCAMLR, provides a sys-

The flags of the Antarctic Treaty nations fly at the South Pole Station.

tem to manage antarctic fish and krill. It sets limits on the amounts that can be taken from these waters. In recent years, the treaty nations have been trying to reach an agreement on how to manage the possible development of Antarctica's oil and other mineral resources. So far, they have not been able to agree on a plan, but hope to do so before the treaty is subject to review in 1991. In the meantime, scientists continue to

do research in an effort to determine the effects of oil exploration and other activities on the antarctic environment. They will also carry out research in other important areas, such as studying the "ozone hole" in the earth's atmosphere over the South Pole.

Interest in the natural resources of both the Arctic and Antarctica will keep growing as long as nations need energy for homes, factories, automobiles, and other uses. How will the demands of modern life affect the future of the roof and floor of the world? Today's young people—the next generation of government officials and scientists—will help provide the answers.

Appendix A:
Learning More About
the Arctic and Antarctica

The following activities will help you learn more about the Arctic and Antarctica. Choose one or more to begin working on today.

1. Start a scrapbook about glaciers. Include magazine pictures, newspaper clippings, and pictures you draw. What happens to glaciers when temperatures increase? Why do icebergs break off from glaciers? What damage do they do?

2. Read a book about an early arctic or antarctic explorer. Admiral Robert E. Peary, Dr. Frederick A. Cook, or Admiral Richard E. Byrd are excellent subjects. Why do you think explorers were willing to take risks and endure hardships?

3. Find out more about the animals that live year round in the Arctic and Antarctica. How do they endure these harsh conditions? If you visit a zoo, ask how animals such as polar bears adapt to warmer temperatures of the zoo.

4. Draw pictures showing the "old" and "new" ways in the Arctic. Show the differences in food, clothing, housing, and transportation. Draw some pictures that show the old and the new in the same picture.

Appendix B:
Scientific Names for
Arctic and Antarctic Animals

Chapter	Common Name	Scientific Name
3.	American Golden Plover	*Pluvialis dominica*
	Arctic Ground Squirrel	*Citellus parryi*
	Arctic Fox	*Alopex lagopus*
	Arctic Tern	*Sterna paradisaea*
	Brown Lemming	*Lemmus trimucronatus*
	Canada Goose	*Branta canadensis*
	Caribou	*Rangifer caribou*
	Common Loon	*Gavia immer*
	Common Ptarmigan	*Lagopus mutus*
	Gyrfalcon	*Falco rusticolus*
	Musk Ox	*Ovibos moschatus*

Chapter	Common Name	Scientific Name
	Polar Bear	*Ursus maritimus*
	Raven	*Corvus corax*
	Snow Bunting	*Plectrophenax nivalis*
	Snowy Owl	*Nyctea scandiaca*
	Trumpeter Swan	*Cygnus buccinator*
	Wolf	*Canis lupus*
6.	Bowhead Whale	*Balaena mysticetus*
	Ringed Seal	*Phoca hispida*
	Walrus	*Odobenus rosmarus*
7.	Reindeer	*Rangifer tarandus*
9.	Adélie Penguin	*Pygoscelis adeliae*
	Emperor Penguin	*Aptenodytes forsteri*
	Fin Whale	*Balaenoptera physalus*
	Humpback Whale	*Megaptera novaeangliae*

Chapter	Common Name	Scientific Name
	Killer Whale	*Orcinus orca*
	Leopard Seal	*Hydrurga leptonyx*
	Skua	*Catharacta skua*
	Southern Right Whale	*Eubalaena australis*
	Weddell Seal	*Leptonychotes weddelli*
10.	Storm Petrel	*Oceanites oceanicus*
11.	Red Krill	*Euphausia superba*

 *Glossary*

adaptation (add-ap-TAY-shuhn)—the ability of animals (including human beings) and plants to adjust to changes in their environment

altimeter (al-TIHM-uh-tuhr)—an instrument for measuring altitude

Arctic Ocean—the waters surrounding the North Pole between North America and Eurasia

arctic whiteout—the blending of white, low-lying clouds with the snow-covered ground, which makes it impossible to see the horizon

atoms—the small, basic particles of which all substances are made

aurora australis (aw-RAWR-uh aw-STRAY-lihs)—brilliant glowing and moving lights visible in the night sky in the southern polar regions; the southern lights

aurora borealis (aw-RAWR-uh boh-ree-AL-ihs)—brilliant glowing and moving lights visible in the night sky in northern polar regions; the northern lights

baleen plates—a row of stiff material that hangs like teeth on a comb from each side of the upper jaw of a baleen whale; used to trap small plants and animals

baleen whales—whales that have baleen plates rather than teeth

barometric reading—a measurement of pressure of the atmosphere, used in forecasting the weather

blubber—a layer of thick fat between the skin and muscle layers of whales and other marine animals

dead reckoning—used here to mean calculating the position of an aircraft without using navigational instruments

food chain—the connection among living things within a community in nature where larger animals feed upon smaller animals and plants

geological (jee-uh-LAHJ-uh-kuhl)—relating to geology, the study of the history of the earth as recorded in its rocks

geologist (jee-AHL-uh-jist)—a scientist who studies the history of the earth as recorded in its rocks

glacier—a very large mass of ice formed from compacted snow and moving slowly down a slope

glaciologist (glay-see-AHL-uh-jist)—a scientist who studies glaciers

greenhouse effect—a theory which states that artificially and naturally produced pollutants (such as smoke from burning fossil fuels and from volcanic eruptions) increase the carbon dioxide level in the atmosphere; this traps heat energy from infrared rays which causes a general warming trend in the earth's climate

Gulf Stream—a warm ocean current flowing north from the Gulf of Mexico that merges with the North Atlantic Current near Newfoundland

gyrocompass (JY-roh-kuhm-puhs)—an instrument of navigation

hibernation—the state in which animals "sleep" through the winter months, slowing down their metabolism and living off their body fat

horizon—the line along which the earth and sky appear to meet

humidity reading—a measurement of moisture in the air

iceberg—a mass of floating ice which has broken away from a glacier

ice cap—a glacier covering a large area of land and flowing outward from its center

ice floes—sheets of floating ice

kayak (KY-ak)—used here to describe a small one-person hunting boat

krill—tiny, shrimplike creatures which are the main food of baleen whales

lead—used here to mean a narrow passage in pack ice

lichen (LY-kuhn)—a plant that is a combination of algae and fungi

mammal—a warm-blooded animal that nurses its young with milk from the mother's body

metabolism—the sum of the chemical and physical processes by which cells produce the materials and energy necessary for the maintenance of life

migrate—to move from one region to another at certain seasons

molecules—the smallest particles into which a substance can be divided and still have the chemical properties of the original; small groups of atoms

motor sailer—a ship with both a motor and sails

North Pole—the northernmost point of the earth; 90° latitude north

nutrients (NYU-tree-ents)—substances that promote the growth of living things

nutritionist (nyu-TRISH-uh-nist)—a scientist who studies different foods and how the body uses them

ozone hole—an area of the ozone layer where the concentration of ozone molecules is especially thin

ozone layer—a layer of the atmosphere which is made up of ozone molecules; this layer screens out ultraviolet rays that would burn and destroy plants, animals, and people

pack ice—broken, floating ice

periscope—an instrument that can be extended above a submarine to observe conditions above the water

permafrost—permanently frozen subsoil in the arctic and antarctic regions

phytoplankton (fy-toh-PLANK-tuhn)—microscopic plants that drift in the water in great numbers

polynias (poh-LIHN-ee-uhs)—large areas of open water surrounded by ice

precipitation (prih-sihp-uh-TAY-shuhn)—condensed water vapor that falls as rain, hail, or snow

predator (PREHD-uh-tuhr)—an animal that kills and eats another animal

rookery (ROOK-uh-ree)—used here to mean a nesting area for a colony of penguins

rotation—used here to mean the earth's movement or spin on its axis

solar radiation—energy given off by the sun in the form of heat and light (including ultraviolet and infrared light)

sonar—a device for locating objects by means of sound waves

South Pole—the southernmost point of the earth; 90° latitude south

tendon—a cord of tissue that connects a muscle and bone

trawler—a boat with a strong fishing net for dragging along the sea bottom

tundra—the land bordering the arctic ice cap and reaching south to the edge of the northern forests

umiak (OO-mee-ak)—a flat-bottomed, lightweight, durable boat used for hunting in arctic waters

visibility—the distance one can see under certain weather conditions

 # Selected Bibliography

Bare, Colleen Stanley. *Rabbits and Hares.* New York: Dodd, Mead, 1983.

Beebe, B. F. *American Wolves, Coyotes, and Foxes.* New York: David McKay, 1964.

Begley, Sharon with John Carey and Mary Bruno. "How Animals Weather Winter." *Newsweek* (February 28, 1983).

Brower, Kenneth. "Two Worlds of the Harp Seal: Above and Beneath the Arctic Ice." *Smithsonian* (July 1979).

Brown, Bruce. "Seal Hunters: Life and Death at the Breathing Hole." *Oceans* (May/June 1981).

Bruemmer, Fred. "The Polar Eskimos: The World's Most Northerly People." *Oceans* (May/June 1981).

———. "Born Again: An Arctic Spring." *Oceans* (July/August 1979).

Dyson, John. *The Hot Arctic.* New York: Little, Brown, 1979.

Eberle, Irmengarde. *Penguins Live Here.* New York: Doubleday, 1974.

Ellis, William S. "Will Oil and Tundra Mix?" *National Geographic* (October 1971).

Greenough, James W. "The Cold War of Little Diomede: An Eskimo Village on the Edge of Today." *Oceans* (May/June 1981).

Hackett, George. "A Trek to the Top of the World." *Newsweek* (May 19, 1986).

Hamner, William M. "Krill—Untapped Bounty From the Sea?" *National Geographic* (May 1984).

Kaplan, James. "Acts of Courage." *Vogue* (March 1987).

Larson, Thor. "Polar Bear: Lonely Nomad of the North." *National Geographic* (April 1971).

McKean, Kevin S. "Mammals of the Sea." *Modern Maturity* (October/November 1984).

Mills, William. "White Lords of the Arctic." *Sea Frontiers* (November/December 1984).

Nicol, Stephen. "Krill Swarms in the Bay of Fundy." *Sea Frontiers* (July/August 1984).

Parfit, Michael. *South Light.* New York: Macmillan, 1985.

Peterson, Roger Tory. "Penguins and Their Neighbors." *National Geographic* (August 1977).

Proctor, Noble S. "Sea Birds of the North: Where Man Cannot Follow." *Oceans* (May/June 1981).

Rahn, Kenneth A. "Who's Polluting the Arctic?" *Natural History* (May 1984).

Ramirez-Heil, Celia. "Antarctica: Life at the End of the Earth." *Americas* (November/December 1981).

Reday, Ladislaw. "The Pull of the Pole: In Search of True North." *Oceans* (January 1985).

Rink, Paul. *Conquering Antarctica: Admiral Richard E. Byrd.* Chicago: Encyclopaedia Britannica Press, 1961.

Steger, Will. "North to the Pole." *National Geographic* (September 1986).

Underwood, Larry S. "Outfoxing the Arctic Cold." *Natural History* (December 1983).

Walsh, James P. "Auguries From Antarctica." *Oceans* (July/August 1982).

Warner, Gale. "Staking Claims on the Last Frontier." *Sierra* (July/August 1984).

Wilsher, Peter and Parin Janmohamed. "Opening the Last Frontier: Managing the Riches of the Polar Regions." *World Press Review* (February 1986).

 *Index*

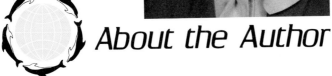

About the Author

Alice Gilbreath is the author of more than twenty books for young people during a twenty-five year writing career. She has written four other Ocean World books: *The Continental Shelf: An Underwater Frontier; The Great Barrier Reef: A Treasure in the Sea; River in the Ocean: The Story of the Gulf Stream;* and *Ring of Fire: And the Hawaiian Islands and Iceland.*

Ms. Gilbreath attended Trinity University in San Antonio, the University of Tulsa, and the College of Idaho. She lives in Bartlesville, Oklahoma.